12-WEEK GUIDED S.

MW00633731

Rest & Reflect

*A Space for Conversations
with Your Creator about Your
Identity, Purpose, and Belonging*

RACHEL FAHRENBACH

REST & REFLECT: 12-WEEK GUIDED SABBATH JOURNAL

COPYRIGHT © 2021 RACHEL FAHRENBACH

Scripture quotations marked (ESV) are from The ESV® Bible
(The Holy Bible, English Standard Version®), copyright © 2001 by
Crossway, a publishing ministry of Good News Publishers. Used by
permission. All rights reserved.

Scripture quotations taken from the (NASB®) New American
Standard Bible®, Copyright © 1960, 1971, 1977, 1995, 2020 by
The Lockman Foundation. Used by permission. All rights reserved.
www.lockman.org

Cover & Interior Design: Rachel Fahrenbach with help from a
community of Hope*Writers, family, and friends.

Cover Image: Yuliya Derbisheva-stock.adobe.com

ISBN 978-1-7368555-1-5 (paperback)

Rachel Fahrenbach
rachelfahrenbach.com

For Steve, Payton, Carter, and Trevor
*God tied the gift of Sabbath with an exquisite bow
when He purposed that I should observe it each week
with the four of you.*

contents

introduction

About five years ago, I experienced a transition year in my life that forced me to wrestle with the concepts of identity, purpose, and belonging. If I was not a great mom, a good friend, a strong ministry leader, or a successful writer—and at that time, all of those things seemed to be in jeopardy—who was I exactly?

My existential crisis was met with the instruction to "just be yourself" and to "stop worrying what other people think of you" and, this one hit hard, "maybe you just need to pray for contentment."

"It isn't contentment I need," I wanted to yell in response, "it's clarity." Jesus had taken me on a journey that, while quite the adventure, contained pieces from different puzzles. Nothing fit together and yet they were supposed to. The fact that I couldn't see exactly how was just salt in the wound. It was a given that I was loved, redeemed, valued, and accepted by Jesus and His work on the cross, but how did that translate into the everyday? What did it mean to be created on purpose with a purpose when my life seemed like the human version of a mixed tape?

Eventually, I stopped writing.

This might seem insignificant if you don't process your thoughts through writing, but to stop meant I gave up on trying to understand who I was and what I was meant to do.

During that same timeframe, conversations around rest and observing the Sabbath seemed to pop up frequently within Bible studies I attended and in casual interactions with friends. After much discussion, study, and prayer, my husband and I decided to incorporate an intentional 24-hour Sabbath practice into our week.

As I studied the concept of Sabbath in the scriptures, I became very aware of God's role as Creator and how we reflect His image when we create (work) for six days and then rest and dwell in that creation on the seventh. In the quiet of Sabbath, I started having weekly conversations with my Creator about His design and desire for my life. He tenderly gave me fresh eyes to see myself the way He sees me and fresh ears to hear His purpose for my life.

As a creative, an Enneagram 6w7, a highly sensitive person, and a host of other labels I won't go into right now, I both take in a lot of information and feel a lot of things about life and the people around me—sometimes all at the same time in the same breath. I found Sabbath gave me a designated time to process that reality with my Creator. Often, I don't even realize all I've been clutching tight to my heart throughout the week until I'm sitting in my chair with my journal answering my Sabbath reflection questions.

This space of reflection is different from daily prayer time, Bible study, or Sunday morning worship. Just like work has a place in the week, there is a time to study the scriptures. Sabbath, though, is the space in which we get to sit in the scriptures and let them wrap their blanket of rest around us. I know I'm not the only one who can get trapped inside my head mulling over things. When left to my own thoughts, I can go down some deep rabbit holes and get lost. But, within this gift of space to process with my Creator, those thoughts untangle within the safety of His love, peace, and truth.

This is my prayer for you as well as you move through this journal. I want you to experience the richness of having your own time of conversing with your Creator about His design and purpose for your life.

HOW TO USE THIS JOURNAL

While this journal is intended to be used daily, the main emphasis is on using it to guide your conversations with your Creator about your identity, purpose, and belonging during your Sabbath practice.

I set up each week with a rhythm of restful and reflective moments, culminating on Sabbath with a deeper reflection time and a Sabbath prayer.

Sabbath

Before you begin, you'll need to decide which day of the week you'll be observing Sabbath. In the Jewish tradition, Sabbath begins at sundown on Friday, but over the centuries, the Christian tradition has designated Sunday morning as the Sabbath. Our family currently observes Sabbath from mid-afternoon Saturday through mid-afternoon Sunday. Which day you observe Sabbath doesn't matter (though I would highly encourage you to make it a full 24-hours) as much as designating a day and committing to it. Pick the day, carve out the time on your calendar to do it, and then observe it!

When considering your Sabbath day, be sure to allocate time to work through this journal. It is helpful, though not required, to sit in the same spot each week while doing your reflection time. This will cue your body and mind into the fact that it's time to rest and reflect.

During your Sabbath Reflection time, you'll take a look back on your week and reflect on questions that relate to the concepts of identity, purpose, and belonging. This time can take as long or as little as you'd like. I personally give it an hour, but you are welcome to do whatever works best for you.

Day One - Day Six

Each week begins with one of four questions. We will be cycling through these four questions three times each over the next 12 weeks:

Who am I?
Who does God say I am?
How should I live?
How should I relate to those around me?

A short devotional will follow with some thoughts to consider and a truth to rest in. Then, you will be given the opportunity to prayerfully consider what that truth means for your own life.

Days three through six will give you space to continue to converse through prayer with your Creator about your thoughts concerning that week's topic. You also will be given space to write down prayer requests for that day.

A *Few Logistics*

If you received this journal without a full week before your Sabbath, you can either begin right away and skip a few days of prayer or wait until the first day after your Sabbath.

You'll want to have easy access to your Bible when you're working through the journal (I personally use a few Bible reading apps on my phone instead of a physical Bible) to go deeper if you have time. I intentionally kept the scripture references to a minimum in this space, not because I don't value scripture, but rather because I wanted the focus to be on prayer and reflection during this time. Sometimes, we can get caught up in the headspace of reading the scriptures, and we forget to engage with the Holy Spirit in understanding them.

If you'd like more resources on the concept of Sabbath or how to implement a Sabbath observance of your own visit:

rachelfahrenbach.com/journal-resources

It really is that simple: pick a Sabbath day, commit to it, read and pray a little bit each day, and then spend time at the end of your week resting and reflecting. Easy peasy, but the return from the time spent is so significant!

Blessings to you as you begin this journey of resting and reflecting over the next 12 weeks!

Rachel

week 1

who am I?

Then the Lord God formed the man of dust from the ground and breathed into his nostrils the breath of life, and the man became a living creature. Genesis 2:7 (ESV)

When I imagine what it was like in the moment God created Adam, it is less children's storybook and more raw intimacy.

A meeting of the Knower and the one to be known.

Sometimes, I imagine Adam laying in the dirt where his body has just been formed like a project freshly sculpted, and sometimes, I imagine him suspended in mid-air like an art piece being added to by the painter. Either way, his body is dull and gray—not decayed flesh but lifeless.

Then: the closeness of God in his nostrils. An intimacy stirring. Adam was not simply comatose and awakened with breath on his face. No, an active, life-giving, energy-creating, all-systems-go breath engaged his mind, his senses, his organs, and his soul. He became a living creature. Not just something in this world, but something part of it, tied to it in both tangible and spiritual ways. Different from every other created thing on earth, not just in his design but in his purpose.

While all of creation sings the praises of God, humanity was uniquely created to reflect the image of its Creator. This purpose is mentioned often throughout both the Old and New Testaments. Most of us understand this on a basic level: we are the hands and feet of Jesus, we point others to God, we are a beacon of hope in a dark world...

But, I would like to suggest we sit in this truth this week: we were uniquely designed to reflect God's image not only in word and deed but in our very being, our very existence.

Each life that walks this earth reflects the image of the Creator, His character, His heart, and His love. His being is infinite and the variations within His creation emphasize that. Including you.

Your being has value and purpose. Your uniqueness was a calculated decision by your Creator. Your personality. Your talents. Your perspective. Your desires. Your goals.

You are not an anomaly.

You are not a mistake.

You were not just plopped into some storyline as an extra meant to take up space but make no real contribution. Or worse yet, left on your own and forgotten. You are known by your Knower. His breath of life engaged your mind, your senses, your organs, and your very soul into existence.

Embrace your unique design.

rest in this truth:

Who am I?
I am a uniquely designed individual.

day one: reflect

Do I think of my uniqueness as an intentional design by God?

Jesus, _____

_____

_____

_____

_____

_____

_____

_____

_____

_____

_____

_____

_____

_____ Amen.

day one: rest

List your concerns and requests below and
then turn them over to your Creator in
prayer, resting in His faithfulness.

Things on my mind today:

- _____
- _____
- _____
- _____
- _____

People on my mind today:

- _____
- _____
- _____
- _____
- _____

day two: reflect

Reflect on the following question with
your Creator during your prayer time:

How am I different from those around me?

Jesus, _____

_____

_____

_____

_____

_____

_____

_____

_____

_____

_____

_____

_____

_____ Amen.

day two: rest

List your concerns and requests below and then turn them over to your Creator in prayer, resting in His faithfulness.

Things on my mind today:

- _____
- _____
- _____
- _____
- _____

People on my mind today:

- _____
- _____
- _____
- _____
- _____

day three: reflect

---

*Reflect on the following question with
your Creator during your prayer time:*

Do I view my differences as a strength? Why or why not?

Jesus, _____

_____

_____

_____

_____

_____

_____

_____

_____

_____

_____

_____

_____ Amen.

day three: rest

List your concerns and requests below and then turn them over to your Creator in prayer, resting in His faithfulness.

Things on my mind today:

- _____
- _____
- _____
- _____
- _____

People on my mind today:

- _____
- _____
- _____
- _____
- _____

day four: reflect

What things come naturally for me?

Jesus, _____

_____

_____

_____

_____

_____

_____

_____

_____

_____

_____

_____

_____ Amen.

day four: rest

List your concerns and requests below and
then turn them over to your Creator in
prayer, resting in His faithfulness.

Things on my mind today:

- _____
- _____
- _____
- _____
- _____

People on my mind today:

- _____
- _____
- _____
- _____
- _____

day five: reflect

*Reflect on the following question with
your Creator during your prayer time:*

In what types of situations do I feel like I shine?

Jesus, _____

_____

_____

_____

_____

_____

_____

_____

_____

_____

_____

_____

_____ Amen.

day five: rest

List your concerns and requests below and then turn them over to your Creator in prayer, resting in His faithfulness.

Things on my mind today:

- _____
- _____
- _____
- _____
- _____

People on my mind today:

- _____
- _____
- _____
- _____
- _____

day six: reflect

What parts of my personality do I appreciate?

Jesus, _____

_____

_____

_____

_____

_____

_____

_____

_____

_____

_____

_____

_____

_____ Amen.

day six: rest

List your concerns and requests below and
then turn them over to your Creator in
prayer, resting in His faithfulness.

Things on my mind today:

- _____
- _____
- _____
- _____
- _____

People on my mind today:

- _____
- _____
- _____
- _____
- _____

sermon notes

speaker:

passage:

main points:

resources mentioned:

to further explore:

reflect: weekly lookback

Use this space to reflect on this past week
during your Sabbath reflection time.

what I embraced:

how God embraced me:

what I hope for next week:

reflect: dig deeper

This list of questions will be the same from week to week. Choose at least 3 questions that jump out to you (you can always do more!). Don't avoid the questions that seem harder to answer; sitting with your Creator with the hard questions is part of the practice of reflection.

who am I?

What did I spend my time doing this week?

What do I want to do more of?

What do I want to do less of?

What is something new I want to try this coming week?

What energized me this week?

What surprised me about myself this week?

who does God say I am?

What did God remind me about myself this week?

What rang true for me this week about who God says I am?

What did I have a hard time believing about my relationship with God this week?

What label did I give myself this week?

What God-given label do I want to speak over myself this week?

how should I live?

Where did I fall short this week?

Where has God been renewing and restoring in my life?

When did I use my God-given talents or giftings this week?

What do I want to converse with God about regarding my future?

What am I hesitant to discuss with God about my future? Why?

What step of obedience do I need to take this week?

how should I relate to those around me?

Who impacted me this week?

Who did I feel the most myself around this week?

Who do I want to be intentional in spending time with this coming week?

Who do I need to release?

How did I support my community this week?

How did my community support me this week?

reflect: dig deeper

Pick three questions from the list to the left to guide you in further reflecting on certain aspects of your identity, purpose, and belonging this week.

reflect: dig deeper

This space is for you to write down any
additional reflections you may
have from the week.

_____

_____

_____

_____

_____

_____

_____

_____

_____

_____

_____

_____

_____

_____

_____

_____

day seven: rest in His provision

As we close out this week of rest & reflection, note below where your Creator answered prayer and give thanks for His enduring love, forgiveness, and faithful provision.

Answered prayers:

- _____

- _____

- _____

Jesus, I thank you this week for:

- _____

- _____

- _____

a sabbath prayer

Jesus, as we physically rest today, may we spiritually rest in the knowledge that your death and resurrection both satisfied and redeemed. We thank you for the ways you continue to provide for our needs on a daily basis. Your faithfulness is steadfast. Your love, enduring. Thank you for the ways you are redeeming and making right the world and our relationships within it. We long for the day when creation will be restored to its original design. Until then, we rest in your goodness, mercy, and grace. Amen.

week 2

who does God say I am?

But now, this is what the Lord says, He who is your Creator, Jacob, and He who formed you, Israel: "Do not fear, for I have redeemed you; I have called you by name; you are Mine!" Isaiah 43:1 (NASB)

We established last week that your Creator uniquely designed you. Your personality, talents, perspective, and ideals are unique from the next person, but have you considered that your redemption is unique as well?

Just as creation was general in its execution yet specific in its implementation, Jesus' work on the cross was for all and specific to one. Your redemption is unique. I like to say that when Adam and Eve sinned, their identities were fractured. I use the word fractured instead of "broken" because when an object is broken, it stops working. We very much continue to function, however, we don't live and love others in the beautiful and full way our Creator intended for us, and sometimes the fracture causes hurt.

Adam and Eve were still very much living creatures with a unique design and unique purpose, but after their choice to sin, they were in need of unique redemption. Eve's choice was a sin of distrust and Adam's a sin of passivity. Both sinned. Both needed redemption. Both were covered by the death and resurrection of Christ. The offer of the forgiveness of sin is the same for everyone, but the act of forgiveness is individual.

Why is this important?

Why does it matter that your redemption is unique?

When we look at the world around us, we see the workmanship of God, the beauty of His craftsmanship, the diversity of His artistry. But, we also see the fracture of sin; some things operate just slightly off from their original design and others far from it. Not everything is quite right and not everything is quite the way it should be.

You know this on a personal level. You recognize the unique design in your life. You see the ordained talents and skills you possess and you are familiar with your strengths. You are also intimately aware of your weaknesses, your struggles, and your sin. You know your life is not quite right, that it is not quite the way it should be; sin has fractured it.

When you are so aware of how far below the bar you fall, it is tempting to discount your contribution to this life and to disqualify yourself from your unique purpose.

Here's the thing: ultimately, this is not about you, or what you can do, or what you will possibly accomplish. Your qualification to reflect the image of your Creator is not measured in your abilities or the execution of them. Your qualification is measured in your design and your redemption by your Creator.

You have value because you are created in the image of God.

You have purpose because you are created in the image of God.

You have redemption because you are created in the image of God.

Sin may have fractured the creation, but the Creator gave His life so that His creation may be restored to rightness and wholeness. He did not blanket the world in generalized forgiveness; your redemption is unique, personal, and intimate.

You are His. You are known, loved, and named, both in design and in redemption.

rest in this truth:

Who does God say I am?
I am a uniquely redeemed individual.

day one: reflect

*Reflect on the following question with
your Creator during your prayer time:*

Do I think about my redemption as unique?

Jesus, _____

_____

_____

_____

_____

_____

_____

_____

_____

_____

_____

_____

_____

_____ Amen.

day one: rest

List your concerns and requests below and
then turn them over to your Creator in
prayer, resting in His faithfulness.

Things on my mind today:

- _____
- _____
- _____
- _____
- _____

People on my mind today:

- _____
- _____
- _____
- _____
- _____

day two: reflect

Reflect on the following question with
your Creator during your prayer time:

Where do I see my unique design fractured the most?

Jesus, ——————————————————————————————

———————————————————————————————————

———————————————————————————————————

———————————————————————————————————

———————————————————————————————————

———————————————————————————————————

———————————————————————————————————

———————————————————————————————————

———————————————————————————————————

———————————————————————————————————

———————————————————————————————————

———————————————————————————————————

——————————————————————————— Amen.

day two: rest

List your concerns and requests below and then turn them over to your Creator in prayer, resting in His faithfulness.

Things on my mind today:

- _____
- _____
- _____
- _____
- _____

People on my mind today:

- _____
- _____
- _____
- _____
- _____

day three: reflect

*Reflect on the following question with
your Creator during your prayer time:*

Do I feel qualified to do the things God is calling me to do?
Why or why not?

Jesus, ——————————————————————————

———————————————————————————————

———————————————————————————————

———————————————————————————————

———————————————————————————————

———————————————————————————————

———————————————————————————————

———————————————————————————————

———————————————————————————————

———————————————————————————————

———————————————————————————————

———————————————————————————————

———————————————————————— Amen.

day three: rest

List your concerns and requests below and then turn them over to your Creator in prayer, resting in His faithfulness.

Things on my mind today:

- _____
- _____
- _____
- _____
- _____

People on my mind today:

- _____
- _____
- _____
- _____
- _____

day four: reflect

*Reflect on the following question with
your Creator during your prayer time:*

Am I resting in the unique redemption Jesus has given me,
or am I still striving to do it on my own?

Jesus, _____

_____

_____

_____

_____

_____

_____

_____

_____

_____

_____

_____

_____

_____

_____ Amen.

day four: rest

List your concerns and requests below and
then turn them over to your Creator in
prayer, resting in His faithfulness.

Things on my mind today:

- _____
- _____
- _____
- _____
- _____

People on my mind today:

- _____
- _____
- _____
- _____
- _____

day five: reflect

What parts of my fractured design do I still need to
release to my Creator so He can restore them?

Jesus, _____

_____

_____

_____

_____

_____

_____

_____

_____

_____

_____

_____

_____ Amen.

day five: rest

List your concerns and requests below and then turn them over to your Creator in prayer, resting in His faithfulness.

Things on my mind today:

- _____
- _____
- _____
- _____
- _____

People on my mind today:

- _____
- _____
- _____
- _____
- _____

day six: reflect

How has my unique redemption affected my relationships?

Jesus, _____

_____

_____

_____

_____

_____

_____

_____

_____

_____

_____

_____

_____

_____ Amen.

day six: rest

List your concerns and requests below and then turn them over to your Creator in prayer, resting in His faithfulness.

Things on my mind today:

- _____
- _____
- _____
- _____
- _____

People on my mind today:

- _____
- _____
- _____
- _____
- _____

sermon notes

speaker:

passage:

main points:

resources mentioned:

to further explore:

reflect: weekly lookback

Use this space to reflect on this past week
during your Sabbath reflection time.

what I embraced:

how God embraced me:

what I hope for next week:

reflect: dig deeper

This list of questions will be the same from week to week. Choose at least 3 questions that jump out to you (you can always do more!). Don't avoid the questions that seem harder to answer; sitting with your Creator with the hard questions is part of the practice of reflection.

who am I?

What did I spend my time doing this week?

What do I want to do more of?

What do I want to do less of?

What is something new I want to try this coming week?

What energized me this week?

What surprised me about myself this week?

who does God say I am?

What did God remind me about myself this week?

What rang true for me this week about who God says I am?

What did I have a hard time believing about my relationship with God this week?

What label did I give myself this week?

What God-given label do I want to speak over myself this week?

how should I live?

Where did I fall short this week?

Where has God been renewing and restoring in my life?

When did I use my God-given talents or giftings this week?

What do I want to converse with God about regarding my future?

What am I hesitant to discuss with God about my future? Why?

What step of obedience do I need to take this week?

how should I relate to those around me?

Who impacted me this week?

Who did I feel the most myself around this week?

Who do I want to be intentional in spending time with this coming week?

Who do I need to release?

How did I support my community this week?

How did my community support me this week?

reflect: dig deeper

Pick three questions from the list to the left to
guide you in further reflecting on certain aspects
of your identity, purpose, and belonging this week.

reflect: dig deeper

This space is for you to write down any
additional reflections you may
have from the week.

_____

_____

_____

_____

_____

_____

_____

_____

_____

_____

_____

_____

_____

day seven: rest in His provision

As we close out this week of rest & reflection, note below where your Creator answered prayer and give thanks for His enduring love, forgiveness, and faithful provision.

Answered prayers:

- _____
- _____
- _____

Jesus, I thank you this week for:

- _____
- _____
- _____

a sabbath prayer

Jesus, as this week comes to an end, may we remember that you came to overcome the darkness of sin through your death and resurrection. You are our Sabbath rest. Your death and resurrection bought us our freedom. May we rest in the provision of your sacrifice, reflect on your goodness and faithfulness, and rejoice as children of God! Amen.

week 3

how should I live?

"Before I formed you in the womb I knew you, before you were born I set you apart; I appointed you as a prophet to the nations."
Jeremiah 1:5 (ESV)

Do you have an unsettledness that you just can't seem to shake out of your bones? Heartstrings you can't seem to untangle from around a dream? A relentless, subtle tapping on an idea in your mind? A warmth that spreads from your soul to your fingertips when you treat your hopes as a friend instead of a foe?

And yet, a voice materializes in the mouth of a friend, in the sentence on the page, in a sound bite from the pulpit, telling you to be thankful for...

...your spouse
...your kids
...your house
...your car
...your community
...your life
...your haves.

You look and internalize "I am discontent." Before you purchase a gratitude journal, let me offer this for your consideration:

Perhaps, that unsettled restlessness is less an unrealized want and more an un-utilized part of your unique design. A gifted purpose from your Creator. Not just a calling, but a compulsion.

Perhaps, what you are feeling is less about your present circumstances, even less about what you want for your future circumstances, and more about your soul's drive to be obedient to the Creator who gave it direction.

Your unique design is set in place to support a unique purpose: to be an image-bearer of the Creator. Being an image-bearer is not a rote, systematic execution of a role. It is as unique as the individual creation living into it. It is both discovery and development. Both self-awareness and spirit-awareness. It is an intimate conversation between Creator and created. Perhaps you are unsettled not because you have not, but because you have not done yet.

The what of your purpose is a given:
- Love the Lord your God with everything within you
- Share the Gospel
- Love your neighbor as yourself
- Care for the widow and orphan in their distress
- Speak out for justice

The how of your purpose is unique:
- Your work
- Your play
- Your rest
- Your worship
- Your family
- Your friendships

Perhaps, you are unsettled because your soul still has more opportunities to reflect the image of its Creator in the unique how of your purpose, and your soul knows it.

rest in this truth:

How should I live?
Within my unique purpose.

day one: reflect

Reflect on the following question with
your Creator during your prayer time:

What did I want to grow up to be when I was ten?
When I was a teen? In my early 20s? Now?

Jesus, _____

_____

_____

_____

_____

_____

_____

_____

_____

_____

_____

_____

_____

_____ Amen.

day one: rest

List your concerns and requests below and then turn them over to your Creator in prayer, resting in His faithfulness.

Things on my mind today:

- _____
- _____
- _____
- _____
- _____

People on my mind today:

- _____
- _____
- _____
- _____
- _____

day two: reflect

*Reflect on the following question with
your Creator during your prayer time:*

What dream did I have to let go of? Why?

Jesus, _____

_____

_____

_____

_____

_____

_____

_____

_____

_____

_____

_____

_____

_____ Amen.

day two: rest

List your concerns and requests below and then turn them over to your Creator in prayer, resting in His faithfulness.

Things on my mind today:

- _____
- _____
- _____
- _____
- _____

People on my mind today:

- _____
- _____
- _____
- _____
- _____

day three: reflect

*Reflect on the following question with
your Creator during your prayer time:*

What roles do I carry today?

Jesus, ————————————————————————————

———————————————————————————————————

———————————————————————————————————

———————————————————————————————————

———————————————————————————————————

———————————————————————————————————

———————————————————————————————————

———————————————————————————————————

———————————————————————————————————

———————————————————————————————————

———————————————————————————————————

———————————————————————————————————

———————————————————————————————— Amen.

day three: rest

List your concerns and requests below and then turn them over to your Creator in prayer, resting in His faithfulness.

Things on my mind today:

- _____
- _____
- _____
- _____
- _____

People on my mind today:

- _____
- _____
- _____
- _____
- _____

day four: reflect

*Reflect on the following question with
your Creator during your prayer time:*

If I didn't have to worry about anything,
what would I do with my life?

Jesus, _____

_____

_____

_____

_____

_____

_____

_____

_____

_____

_____

_____ Amen.

day four: rest

List your concerns and requests below and
then turn them over to your Creator in
prayer, resting in His faithfulness.

Things on my mind today:

- _____
- _____
- _____
- _____
- _____

People on my mind today:

- _____
- _____
- _____
- _____
- _____

day five: reflect

When have I felt the most like myself and energized?

Jesus, _____

_____

_____

_____

_____

_____

_____

_____

_____

_____

_____

_____ Amen.

day five: rest

List your concerns and requests below and
then turn them over to your Creator in
prayer, resting in His faithfulness.

Things on my mind today:

- _____
- _____
- _____
- _____
- _____

People on my mind today:

- _____
- _____
- _____
- _____
- _____

day six: reflect

*Reflect on the following question with
your Creator during your prayer time:*

Where in my life do I feel unsettled?

Jesus, _____

_____

_____

_____

_____

_____

_____

_____

_____

_____

_____

_____

_____ Amen.

day six: rest

List your concerns and requests below and then turn them over to your Creator in prayer, resting in His faithfulness.

Things on my mind today:

- _____
- _____
- _____
- _____
- _____

People on my mind today:

- _____
- _____
- _____
- _____
- _____

sermon notes

speaker:

passage:

main points:

resources mentioned:

to further explore:

reflect: weekly lookback

Use this space to reflect on this past week
during your Sabbath reflection time.

what I embraced:

how God embraced me:

what I hope for next week:

reflect: dig deeper

This list of questions will be the same from week to week. Choose at least 3 questions that jump out to you (you can always do more!). Don't avoid the questions that seem harder to answer; sitting with your Creator with the hard questions is part of the practice of reflection.

who am I?

What did I spend my time doing this week?

What do I want to do more of?

What do I want to do less of?

What is something new I want to try this coming week?

What energized me this week?

What surprised me about myself this week?

who does God say I am?

What did God remind me about myself this week?

What rang true for me this week about who God says I am?

What did I have a hard time believing about my relationship with God this week?

What label did I give myself this week?

What God-given label do I want to speak over myself this week?

how should I live?

Where did I fall short this week?

Where has God been renewing and restoring in my life?

When did I use my God-given talents or giftings this week?

What do I want to converse with God about regarding my future?

What am I hesitant to discuss with God about my future? Why?

What step of obedience do I need to take this week?

how should I relate to those around me?

Who impacted me this week?

Who did I feel the most myself around this week?

Who do I want to be intentional in spending time with this coming week?

Who do I need to release?

How did I support my community this week?

How did my community support me this week?

reflect: dig deeper

Pick three questions from the list to the left to
guide you in further reflecting on certain aspects
of your identity, purpose, and belonging this week.

reflect: dig deeper

This space is for you to write down any
additional reflections you may
have from the week.

day seven: rest in His provision

As we close out this week of rest & reflection, note below where your Creator answered prayer and give thanks for His enduring love, forgiveness, and faithful provision.

Answered prayers:

- _____
- _____
- _____

Jesus, I thank you this week for:

- _____
- _____
- _____

a sabbath prayer

Jesus, may we go into the new week remembering you are holy, good, and faithful. Through you, we have abundant life. Please provide for our needs this week and sustain us when challenges present themselves. Please bless us and draw us closer to you each and every day. Amen.

week 4

how should I relate to those around me?

For everything there is a season, and a
time for every matter under heaven:
Ecclesiastes 3:1 (ESV)

There is a tendency to read Ecclesiastes 3:1 as if we are in rest and God calls us into action in the right time to do the one thing He created us to do. However, if you continue to read the rest of the chapter, you'll begin to see a picture of humanity always in action, living out the various facets and roles of our purpose in God's right timing. Why, then, are you afraid to give voice to the role you think your Creator is asking you to embrace right now?

Our unique design, our unique redemption, and our unique purpose work themselves out in our unique positioning. You have been placed in specific roles within specific communities to reflect His image. In a true fatherly manner, our Creator modeled what this looks like for us. Throughout scripture we see God fulfilling many varied roles (judge, son, healer, friend, teacher, storyteller, etc.) yet we are often surprised when we suddenly find ourselves with multiple roles in our own lives. We might even think we're doing something wrong. Our society puts such an emphasis on finding "the one thing that makes you come alive," "the one thing you were meant to do," or "the one thing you could see yourself doing for the rest of your life" that we've mistaken their drive for a label as the directive from our Creator.

If you're looking for your one thing, the good news is that your Creator has already given it to you: image-bearer. But, if you're expecting it to look one way throughout your entire life, then you are missing the depth of creation and your place in it. The One you are designed to reflect holds and executes roles that vary and so will you.

Maybe you feel like if you pursue a specific role, you are choosing yourself over everyone else. Or, perhaps, you're waiting for the energy to be there. Or, you're waiting for the moment that guilt won't eat at the edges of your dream.

The reality is God doesn't grant us seasons to stop living out our purpose, but He does grant us seasons for the different roles He uses to accomplish it. Sometimes a role isn't meant for a certain season, but can I ask you a question? Have you designated it "not the right season" for you to take on a certain role because of fear or uncertainty?

Maybe you have a new baby, or an aging parent, or a rebellious teen, or a job that drains you, or some other commitment, and you can't see how this new role will honor the roles you already have? Maybe you feel like you need to "finish" a sacrificial role that serves someone else before truly embracing the role that feels selfish?

I will tell you this: the best thing you can do for those around you, especially those you love dearly, is to be obedient to the role your Creator designed you for and is calling you into right now. To disobey serves no one, especially the One whose image you're supposed to reflect.

I can't tell you if this is the season for the role you're considering, but I can encourage you to stop dismissing it and bring it to your Creator to ask Him.

rest in this truth:

How should I relate to those around me?
Within my unique positioning.

day one: reflect

*Reflect on the following question with
your Creator during your prayer time:*

What role do I feel called to embrace right now?

Jesus, _____

_____

_____

_____

_____

_____

_____

_____

_____

_____

_____

_____

_____ Amen.

day one: rest

List your concerns and requests below and then turn them over to your Creator in prayer, resting in His faithfulness.

Things on my mind today:

- _____
- _____
- _____
- _____
- _____

People on my mind today:

- _____
- _____
- _____
- _____
- _____

day two: reflect

*Reflect on the following question with
your Creator during your prayer time:*

What role am I running from?

Jesus, _____

_____

_____

_____

_____

_____

_____

_____

_____

_____

_____

_____

_____ Amen.

day two: rest

List your concerns and requests below and then turn them over to your Creator in prayer, resting in His faithfulness.

Things on my mind today:

- _____
- _____
- _____
- _____
- _____

People on my mind today:

- _____
- _____
- _____
- _____
- _____

day three: reflect

What roles do I currently have that I love and enjoy?

Jesus, _____

_____

_____

_____

_____

_____

_____

_____

_____

_____

_____

_____ Amen.

day three: rest

List your concerns and requests below and
then turn them over to your Creator in
prayer, resting in His faithfulness.

Things on my mind today:

- _____
- _____
- _____
- _____
- _____

People on my mind today:

- _____
- _____
- _____
- _____
- _____

day four: reflect

*Reflect on the following question with
your Creator during your prayer time:*

What roles do I currently have that drain me?

Jesus, _____

_____

_____

_____

_____

_____

_____

_____

_____

_____

_____

_____

_____ Amen.

day four: rest

List your concerns and requests below and then turn them over to your Creator in prayer, resting in His faithfulness.

Things on my mind today:

- _____
- _____
- _____
- _____
- _____

People on my mind today:

- _____
- _____
- _____
- _____
- _____

day five: reflect

Reflect on the following question with
your Creator during your prayer time:

Who am I afraid of failing if I take on a certain role?

Jesus, _____

_____

_____

_____

_____

_____

_____

_____

_____

_____

_____

_____

_____ Amen.

day five: rest

List your concerns and requests below and
then turn them over to your Creator in
prayer, resting in His faithfulness.

Things on my mind today:

- _____
- _____
- _____
- _____
- _____

People on my mind today:

- _____
- _____
- _____
- _____
- _____

day six: reflect

Do I need to pivot or modify a role I currently have
because of the season of life I am in?

Jesus, _____

_____

_____

_____

_____

_____

_____

_____

_____

_____

_____

_____

_____ Amen.

day six: rest

List your concerns and requests below and then turn them over to your Creator in prayer, resting in His faithfulness.

Things on my mind today:

- _____
- _____
- _____
- _____
- _____

People on my mind today:

- _____
- _____
- _____
- _____
- _____

sermon notes

speaker:

passage:

main points:

resources mentioned:

to further explore:

reflect: weekly lookback

Use this space to reflect on this past week
during your Sabbath reflection time.

what I embraced:

how God embraced me:

what I hope for next week:

reflect: dig deeper

This list of questions will be the same from week to week. Choose at least 3 questions that jump out to you (you can always do more!). Don't avoid the questions that seem harder to answer; sitting with your Creator with the hard questions is part of the practice of reflection.

who am I?

What did I spend my time doing this week?

What do I want to do more of?

What do I want to do less of?

What is something new I want to try this coming week?

What energized me this week?

What surprised me about myself this week?

who does God say I am?

What did God remind me about myself this week?

What rang true for me this week about who God says I am?

What did I have a hard time believing about my relationship with God this week?

What label did I give myself this week?

What God-given label do I want to speak over myself this week?

how should I live?

Where did I fall short this week?

Where has God been renewing and restoring in my life?

When did I use my God-given talents or giftings this week?

What do I want to converse with God about regarding my future?

What am I hesitant to discuss with God about my future? Why?

What step of obedience do I need to take this week?

how should I relate to those around me?

Who impacted me this week?

Who did I feel the most myself around this week?

Who do I want to be intentional in spending time with this coming week?

Who do I need to release?

How did I support my community this week?

How did my community support me this week?

reflect: dig deeper

Pick three questions from the list to the left to
guide you in further reflecting on certain aspects
of your identity, purpose, and belonging this week.

reflect: dig deeper

This space is for you to write down any
additional reflections you may
have from the week.

day seven: rest in His provision

As we close out this week of rest & reflection, note below where your Creator answered prayer and give thanks for His enduring love, forgiveness, and faithful provision.

Answered prayers:

- _____
- _____
- _____

Jesus, I thank you this week for:

- _____
- _____
- _____

a sabbath prayer

Jesus, thank you for the gift of Sabbath and the opportunity it gives to connect with you and with others. As this week draws to a close, open our eyes to those you've placed in our lives to walk alongside us in both our challenges and our dreams. May we acknowledge and receive their support. Please open our hearts to welcome those who need a friend. Open our ears to hear the hurts and needs of others so that we can help in whatever way we are able. And open our lips to speak truth, encouragement, and hope to those around us. Amen.

week 5

who am I?

[Eve] took some of its fruit and ate; and she also
gave some to her husband with her, and he ate.
Then the eyes of both of them were opened, and
they knew that they were naked and they sewed
fig leaves together and made themselves waist
coverings. Genesis 3:6b-7 (NASB)

God dwelled with His creation on the seventh day. Could you
imagine? The One who you were created to reflect dwelling so
intimately with you? You would have no questions about your
identity, your purpose, or your sense of belonging. Living within
such a closeness to your Creator, you'd have no doubt in your mind
who you were, whose you were, and why you were there.

It would be glorious work and exhilarating rest.

But for sin: "she took some of its fruit and ate."

But for the resulting fracture: "Their eyes were opened and they
knew they were naked."

Their fig-leaf waist coverings were a visual representation that
something was off. Before their rebellious act, there was nothing
shameful in their design, it was as the Creator intended and brought
glory to Him. But after? Their design was fractured and the fig leaves
an equivalent of a bandaid on a gushing wound.

Because sin has fractured our unique design, what was meant to
be a reflection of our Creator has become a distraction and, in some
cases, a damaging distortion.

What I've come to learn about myself, and what I hope you learn
too through the coming weeks of reflection, is that my weakness and
my sin-tendency often have a direct correlation to the strengths,
talents, gifting, and uniqueness of my design. For example, one of
the strengths of my unique design is that I feel emotions intensely

and can utilize them in my writing, which deepens it and allows me to connect to a reader. But the fractured version of that: I feel emotions intensely and can at times let them take the wheel, which does not reflect my Creator and can distort my relationships.

It is important for us to analyze and become familiar with our weaknesses, not so we can accept them as-is and give them a home, but in order to allow the Holy Spirit to restore them to their original design. Often we're told to accept our failings and give ourselves grace in the moments we make mistakes. The heart behind that is well-intended, but let's push back on that just a little bit. An acceptance of our fractured design as anything other than it is, a fracture that needs healing and restoration, may make us feel better momentarily but it will not help us live fully into everything our Creator has purposed for us.

We do not need to give ourselves grace, we need to fall on our face and ask Jesus to remind us of the grace He has already given. Then, we need to ask Him to give us the awareness and humility to be part of the restoration process.

rest in this truth:

Who am I?
I am a fractured image of my Creator.

day one: reflect

*Reflect on the following question with
your Creator during your prayer time:*

What would I say are my weaknesses?

Jesus, _____

_____

_____

_____

_____

_____

_____

_____

_____

_____

_____

_____

_____

_____ Amen.

day one: rest

List your concerns and requests below and
then turn them over to your Creator in
prayer, resting in His faithfulness.

Things on my mind today:

- _____
- _____
- _____
- _____
- _____

People on my mind today:

- _____
- _____
- _____
- _____
- _____

day two: reflect

What have others said are my weaknesses?

Jesus, _____

_____

_____

_____

_____

_____

_____

_____

_____

_____

_____

_____

_____

_____ Amen.

day two: rest

List your concerns and requests below and
then turn them over to your Creator in
prayer, resting in His faithfulness.

Things on my mind today:

- _____
- _____
- _____
- _____
- _____

People on my mind today:

- _____
- _____
- _____
- _____
- _____

day three: reflect

*Reflect on the following question with
your Creator during your prayer time:*

What areas of sin in my life have I been convicted about in recent weeks?

Jesus, _____

_____

_____

_____

_____

_____

_____

_____

_____

_____

_____

_____

_____

_____

_____ Amen.

day three: rest

List your concerns and requests below and
then turn them over to your Creator in
prayer, resting in His faithfulness.

Things on my mind today:

- _____
- _____
- _____
- _____
- _____

People on my mind today:

- _____
- _____
- _____
- _____
- _____

day four: reflect

Reflect on the following question with
your Creator during your prayer time:

When in my life has my strength become
a weakness because of sin?

Jesus, _____

_____

_____

_____

_____

_____

_____

_____

_____

_____

_____

_____

_____ Amen.

day four: rest

List your concerns and requests below and
then turn them over to your Creator in
prayer, resting in His faithfulness.

Things on my mind today:

- _____
- _____
- _____
- _____
- _____

People on my mind today:

- _____
- _____
- _____
- _____
- _____

day five: reflect

*Reflect on the following question with
your Creator during your prayer time:*

When in my life have I not reflected
my Creator because of sin?

Jesus, _____

_____

_____

_____

_____

_____

_____

_____

_____

_____

_____

_____

_____ Amen.

day five: rest

List your concerns and requests below and
then turn them over to your Creator in
prayer, resting in His faithfulness.

Things on my mind today:

- _____
- _____
- _____
- _____
- _____

People on my mind today:

- _____
- _____
- _____
- _____
- _____

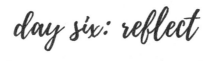

day six: reflect

*Reflect on the following question with
your Creator during your prayer time:*

Where did I fall short this week? Have I confessed
that and asked for forgiveness and restoration?

Jesus,

_____

_____

_____

_____

_____

_____

_____

_____

_____

_____

_____

_____ Amen.

day six: rest

*List your concerns and requests below and
then turn them over to your Creator in
prayer, resting in His faithfulness.*

Things on my mind today:

- _____
- _____
- _____
- _____
- _____

People on my mind today:

- _____
- _____
- _____
- _____
- _____

sermon notes

speaker:

passage:

main points:

resources mentioned:

to further explore:

reflect: weekly lookback

Use this space to reflect on this past week during your Sabbath reflection time.

what I embraced:

how God embraced me:

what I hope for next week:

reflect: dig deeper

This list of questions will be the same from week to week. Choose at least 3 questions that jump out to you (you can always do more!). Don't avoid the questions that seem harder to answer; sitting with your Creator with the hard questions is part of the practice of reflection.

who am I?

What did I spend my time doing this week?

What do I want to do more of?

What do I want to do less of?

What is something new I want to try this coming week?

What energized me this week?

What surprised me about myself this week?

who does God say I am?

What did God remind me about myself this week?

What rang true for me this week about who God says I am?

What did I have a hard time believing about my relationship with God this week?

What label did I give myself this week?

What God-given label do I want to speak over myself this week?

how should I live?

Where did I fall short this week?

Where has God been renewing and restoring in my life?

When did I use my God-given talents or giftings this week?

What do I want to converse with God about regarding my future?

What am I hesitant to discuss with God about my future? Why?

What step of obedience do I need to take this week?

how should I relate to those around me?

Who impacted me this week?

Who did I feel the most myself around this week?

Who do I want to be intentional in spending time with this coming week?

Who do I need to release?

How did I support my community this week?

How did my community support me this week?

reflect: dig deeper

Pick three questions from the list to the left to
guide you in further reflecting on certain aspects
of your identity, purpose, and belonging this week.

reflect: dig deeper

*This space is for you to write down any
additional reflections you may
have from the week.*

day seven: rest in His provision

As we close out this week of rest & reflection, note below where your Creator answered prayer and give thanks for His enduring love, forgiveness, and faithful provision.

Answered prayers:

- _____
- _____
- _____

Jesus, I thank you this week for:

- _____
- _____
- _____

a sabbath prayer

Jesus, as we physically rest today, may we spiritually rest in the knowledge that your death and resurrection both satisfied and redeemed. We thank you for the ways you continue to provide for our needs on a daily basis. Your faithfulness is steadfast. Your love, enduring. Thank you for the ways you are redeeming and making right the world and our relationships within it. We long for the day when creation will be restored to its original design. Until then, we rest in your goodness, mercy, and grace. Amen.

week 6

who does God say I am?

Look at the birds of the air: they neither sow nor reap nor gather into barns, and yet your heavenly Father feeds them. Are you not of more value than they? Matthew 6:26 (ESV)

My resume looks like the product of someone with the inability to focus, but the reality is that much of it has been out of my control. Between career moves for my husband, location moves for our family, and a move into motherhood, the last 15+ years have looked far different than I dreamed up when I submitted my first job application after college. I graduated with the intent to become an editor to pay the bills and a writer to fill my soul. I worked professionally as an editor for less than 4 years right after college and have only recently figured out (and am still refining) what being a working writer means.

During that time I did, however, tutor high school and college students in writing, coordinate numerous weddings and events, co-create and run a non-profit, serve on a leadership team in a church start-up, build multiple websites, create social media platforms for almost every company and ministry I was involved in, help start a podcast for dentists, write skits for church events, and teach a beginner's sign language class to k-2nd graders.

Whew! It's been a whirlwind of activity.

I used to think I had an inability to commit to anything for more than two years. I hated this about myself and considered it a personality flaw. I would fight against any desire to move onto something new for the longest time, worried that I was being finicky and flighty. In fact, I was driving home from volunteering one night and a familiar feeling settled over me, a feeling that it was time for me to move on from volunteering for this particular organization. I started praying against my inability to stick to things (my the-grass-is-always-greener mentality) when the Holy Spirit stopped me in my tracks. He recalled to my mind the lengths of times that I had committed to various things throughout my life. I had to take a hand off the wheel to wipe the tears from my eyes as I realized that I had been believing a lie about myself for years.

Then, He admonished: "Rachel, you move on because I have things I want you to do, want you to learn, and want you to grow in. You move because I ask you to."

The fracture of sin had me believing that I had a personality flaw that needed to be corrected. The truth was that God had strategically placed me in various communities, situations, relationships, and work to fulfill His purposes.

You may be believing a lie about yourself today and need to ask God to reveal the truth from His perspective. Maybe you have been holding onto this lie for years, completely unaware of how you had falsely internalized it as a truth about your identity. Your Creator knows differently and wants you to see yourself as He sees you.

rest in this truth:

Who does God say I am?
I am a uniquely designed individual
who has value and purpose, even
when the fracture of sin makes it
difficult to see it for myself.

day one: reflect

*Reflect on the following question with
your Creator during your prayer time:*

What's a lie I've been believing about myself?

Jesus, _____

_____

_____

_____

_____

_____

_____

_____

_____

_____

_____

_____

_____

_____ Amen.

day one: rest

List your concerns and requests below and
then turn them over to your Creator in
prayer, resting in His faithfulness.

Things on my mind today:

- _____
- _____
- _____
- _____
- _____

People on my mind today:

- _____
- _____
- _____
- _____
- _____

day two: reflect

*Reflect on the following question with
your Creator during your prayer time:*

What is a weakness I feel disqualifies me
from reflecting my Creator's image?

Jesus, _____

_____

_____

_____

_____

_____

_____

_____

_____

_____

_____

_____

_____

_____ Amen.

day two: rest

List your concerns and requests below and then turn them over to your Creator in prayer, resting in His faithfulness.

Things on my mind today:

- _____
- _____
- _____
- _____
- _____

People on my mind today:

- _____
- _____
- _____
- _____
- _____

day three: reflect

Reflect on the following question with
your Creator during your prayer time:

What's one thing about myself I wish I could change?

Jesus, _____

_____

_____

_____

_____

_____

_____

_____

_____

_____

_____

_____

_____

_____ Amen.

day three: rest

List your concerns and requests below and then turn them over to your Creator in prayer, resting in His faithfulness.

Things on my mind today:

- _____
- _____
- _____
- _____
- _____

People on my mind today:

- _____
- _____
- _____
- _____
- _____

day four: reflect

Reflect on the following question with
your Creator during your prayer time:

Is there a part of my character that I wish was different?

Jesus, _____

_____

_____

_____

_____

_____

_____

_____

_____

_____

_____

_____

_____ Amen.

day four: rest

List your concerns and requests below and
then turn them over to your Creator in
prayer, resting in His faithfulness.

Things on my mind today:

- _____
- _____
- _____
- _____
- _____

People on my mind today:

- _____
- _____
- _____
- _____
- _____

day five: reflect

*Reflect on the following question with
your Creator during your prayer time:*

Have I been using the words given to me by someone else
to describe me in a way God wouldn't?

Jesus, _____

_____

_____

_____

_____

_____

_____

_____

_____

_____

_____

_____

_____

_____ Amen.

day five: rest

List your concerns and requests below and then turn them over to your Creator in prayer, resting in His faithfulness.

Things on my mind today:

- _____
- _____
- _____
- _____
- _____

People on my mind today:

- _____
- _____
- _____
- _____
- _____

day six: reflect

*Reflect on the following question with
your Creator during your prayer time:*

Have I asked my Creator if those aspects of my personality
or character that I wish I could change were
designed by Him for a specific purpose?

Jesus, _____

_____

_____

_____

_____

_____

_____

_____

_____

_____

_____

_____

_____

_____ Amen.

day six: rest

List your concerns and requests below and then turn them over to your Creator in prayer, resting in His faithfulness.

Things on my mind today:

- _____
- _____
- _____
- _____
- _____

People on my mind today:

- _____
- _____
- _____
- _____
- _____

sermon notes

speaker:

passage:

main points:

resources mentioned:

to further explore:

reflect: weekly lookback

Use this space to reflect on this past week
during your Sabbath reflection time.

what I embraced:

how God embraced me:

what I hope for next week:

reflect: dig deeper

This list of questions will be the same from week to week. Choose at least 3 questions that jump out to you (you can always do more!). Don't avoid the questions that seem harder to answer; sitting with your Creator with the hard questions is part of the practice of reflection.

who am I?

What did I spend my time doing this week?

What do I want to do more of?

What do I want to do less of?

What is something new I want to try this coming week?

What energized me this week?

What surprised me about myself this week?

who does God say I am?

What did God remind me about myself this week?

What rang true for me this week about who God says I am?

What did I have a hard time believing about my relationship with God this week?

What label did I give myself this week?

What God-given label do I want to speak over myself this week?

how should I live?

Where did I fall short this week?

Where has God been renewing and restoring in my life?

When did I use my God-given talents or giftings this week?

What do I want to converse with God about regarding my future?

What am I hesitant to discuss with God about my future? Why?

What step of obedience do I need to take this week?

how should I relate to those around me?

Who impacted me this week?

Who did I feel the most myself around this week?

Who do I want to be intentional in spending time with this coming week?

Who do I need to release?

How did I support my community this week?

How did my community support me this week?

reflect: dig deeper

Pick three questions from the list to the left to
guide you in further reflecting on certain aspects
of your identity, purpose, and belonging this week.

reflect: dig deeper

This space is for you to write down any
additional reflections you may
have from the week.

day seven: rest in His provision

As we close out this week of rest & reflection, note below where your Creator answered prayer and give thanks for His enduring love, forgiveness, and faithful provision.

Answered prayers:

- _____
- _____
- _____

Jesus, I thank you this week for:

- _____
- _____
- _____

a sabbath prayer

Jesus, as this week comes to an end, may we remember that you came to overcome the darkness of sin through your death and resurrection. You are our Sabbath rest. Your death and resurrection bought us our freedom. May we rest in the provision of your sacrifice, reflect on your goodness and faithfulness, and rejoice as children of God! Amen.

week 7

how should I live?

Not that I have already obtained all this, or have already arrived at my goal, but I press on to take hold of that for which Christ Jesus took hold of me. Philipians 3:12 (ESV)

In the years I co-founded and co-ran a food pantry, I had more than one person tell me exactly what they thought of my personality and leadership skills. If you want to learn all your flaws, start a non-profit fully run by volunteers! When you aren't paying them for their time, people tend to feel more at ease criticizing how the job is being done. While most of the accusations leveled at me came from a place of simply not having the full picture, some of the accusations actually had merit.

One of the legitimate concerns brought to my attention was the fact that I would cut off people with a response before they even had a chance to finish their thought. They felt interrupted, dismissed, and devalued in those moments—something I never intended for them to feel!

I was mortified and set out to analyze what I was doing that would give someone that impression. I realized my ability to take in information and process it quickly (which is an immense strength in decision-making), and my sincere desire to relate, encourage, and help others (which are great strengths when you are running a non-profit), was backfiring on me in these conversations. My strengths were backfiring on me because they had some flaws.

I'll be honest, after one too many conversations where my mistakes and weaknesses were laid out for everyone to discuss, I lamented to my husband that it wasn't worth it. "I'm obviously not good enough to do this role."

Take that in for a moment: I had decided that my involvement in the non-profit that God had placed in my care, and the relationships with clients and volunteers that came with it, were not worth it because I felt like my strengths weren't good enough.

Thankfully, I wasn't leading alone and there were other, wiser, women on the leadership team who came alongside me as mentors. They taught me that we need to be obedient to God's call to use our strengths in the roles He has placed us, despite their flaws. The way to do this? Have a teachable spirit.

1. *Receive* what someone offers (criticism, advice, opinion) and thank them for bringing it to your attention.
2. *Take it to God* in prayer and ask Him to show what is true and what needs to fall to the wayside.
3. *Ask Him* what you should do about it.

Recently, I was tasked by a business coach to ask my friends what they would say is one thing I'm good at. "Listening" was mentioned more than a couple of times! I honestly believe that's because I went to God with the criticism that had been given and asked Him to teach me what was true and what I needed to do about it. My strengths didn't get stronger and my weaknesses less, rather God showed me how to embrace my unique design in a way that is closer to how it was intended if sin hadn't entered the picture. Not perfect—our strengths won't ever be this side of heaven—but with oversight from the Spirit.

rest in this truth:

How should I live?
Within my strengths,
as flawed as they are.

145

day one: reflect

*Reflect on the following question with
your Creator during your prayer time:*

What is one way I rub people wrong? How is a
strength of mine connected to it?

Jesus, _____

_____

_____

_____

_____

_____

_____

_____

_____

_____

_____

_____

_____

_____ Amen.

day one: rest

*List your concerns and requests below and
then turn them over to your Creator in
prayer, resting in His faithfulness.*

Things on my mind today:

- _____
- _____
- _____
- _____
- _____

People on my mind today:

- _____
- _____
- _____
- _____
- _____

day two: reflect

────────────────

*Reflect on the following question with
your Creator during your prayer time:*

When was a time in my life where I thought I was
doing a good job but someone else disagreed?

Jesus, _____

_____

_____

_____

_____

_____

_____

_____

_____

_____

_____

_____

_____

_____ Amen.

day two: rest

List your concerns and requests below and
then turn them over to your Creator in
prayer, resting in His faithfulness.

Things on my mind today:

- _____
- _____
- _____
- _____
- _____

People on my mind today:

- _____
- _____
- _____
- _____
- _____

day three: reflect

*Reflect on the following question with
your Creator during your prayer time:*

Which skill-set of mine seems to be not quite as appreciated by others?

Jesus, _____

_____

_____

_____

_____

_____

_____

_____

_____

_____

_____

_____

_____

_____

_____ Amen.

day three: rest

List your concerns and requests below and then turn them over to your Creator in prayer, resting in His faithfulness.

Things on my mind today:

- _____
- _____
- _____
- _____
- _____

People on my mind today:

- _____
- _____
- _____
- _____
- _____

day four: reflect

*Reflect on the following question with
your Creator during your prayer time:*

Which strength of mine do I need to ask for God's help in refining?

Jesus, _____

_____

_____

_____

_____

_____

_____

_____

_____

_____

_____

_____

_____

_____

_____ Amen.

day four: rest

List your concerns and requests below and
then turn them over to your Creator in
prayer, resting in His faithfulness.

Things on my mind today:

- _____

- _____

- _____

- _____

- _____

People on my mind today:

- _____

- _____

- _____

- _____

- _____

day five: reflect

*Reflect on the following question with
your Creator during your prayer time:*

Who is someone in my life who I can emulate
when it comes to my particular strengths?

Jesus, _____

_____

_____

_____

_____

_____

_____

_____

_____

_____

_____

_____

_____ Amen.

day five: rest

List your concerns and requests below and then turn them over to your Creator in prayer, resting in His faithfulness.

Things on my mind today:

- _____
- _____
- _____
- _____
- _____

People on my mind today:

- _____
- _____
- _____
- _____
- _____

day six: reflect

*Reflect on the following question with
your Creator during your prayer time:*

Am I feeling like my strengths are not good
enough for a role I'm in? Why or why not?

Jesus, ————————————————————————————

_____

_____

_____

_____

_____

_____

_____

_____

_____

_____

_____

_____

_____

_____ Amen.

day six: rest

List your concerns and requests below and
then turn them over to your Creator in
prayer, resting in His faithfulness.

Things on my mind today:

- _____
- _____
- _____
- _____
- _____

People on my mind today:

- _____
- _____
- _____
- _____
- _____

sermon notes

speaker:

passage:

main points:

resources mentioned:

to further explore:

reflect: weekly lookback

Use this space to reflect on this past week
during your Sabbath reflection time.

what I embraced:

how God embraced me:

what I hope for next week:

reflect: dig deeper

This list of questions will be the same from week to week. Choose at least 3 questions that jump out to you (you can always do more!). Don't avoid the questions that seem harder to answer; sitting with your Creator with the hard questions is part of the practice of reflection.

who am I?

What did I spend my time doing this week?

What do I want to do more of?

What do I want to do less of?

What is something new I want to try this coming week?

What energized me this week?

What surprised me about myself this week?

who does God say I am?

What did God remind me about myself this week?

What rang true for me this week about who God says I am?

What did I have a hard time believing about my relationship with God this week?

What label did I give myself this week?

What God-given label do I want to speak over myself this week?

how should I live?

Where did I fall short this week?

Where has God been renewing and restoring in my life?

When did I use my God-given talents or giftings this week?

What do I want to converse with God about regarding my future?

What am I hesitant to discuss with God about my future? Why?

What step of obedience do I need to take this week?

how should I relate to those around me?

Who impacted me this week?

Who did I feel the most myself around this week?

Who do I want to be intentional in spending time with this coming week?

Who do I need to release?

How did I support my community this week?

How did my community support me this week?

reflect: dig deeper

Pick three questions from the list to the left to
guide you in further reflecting on certain aspects
of your identity, purpose, and belonging this week.

reflect: dig deeper

This space is for you to write down any
additional reflections you may
have from the week.

_____

_____

_____

_____

_____

_____

_____

_____

_____

_____

_____

_____

_____

_____

_____

_____

_____

day seven: rest in His provision

As we close out this week of rest & reflection, note below where your Creator answered prayer and give thanks for His enduring love, forgiveness, and faithful provision.

Answered prayers:

- _____
- _____
- _____

Jesus, I thank you this week for:

- _____
- _____
- _____

a sabbath prayer

Jesus, may we go into the new week remembering you are holy, good, and faithful. Through you, we have abundant life. Please provide for our needs this week and sustain us when challenges present themselves. Please bless us and draw us closer to you each and every day. Amen.

week 8

how should I relate to those around me?

> Put on then, as God's chosen ones, holy and beloved, compassionate hearts, kindness, humility, meekness, and patience, bearing with one another and, if one has a complaint against another, forgiving each other; as the Lord has forgiven you, so you also must forgive. Col 3:12-13 (ESV)

As the phrase "social distancing" has become a norm in our daily vocabulary, I'm reminded of an interaction I had with a friend right before Covid-19 became a thing. We met on a mid-week evening for coffee. Little did I know that a month later, in-person coffee dates would be shut-down. At one point in our conversation, we admitted to each other that we had forced ourselves to come because we were tired and the bed seemed more promising than company. We laughed and acknowledged that we were glad we got in our cars and showed up at the restaurant, that the company in fact proved worth it. Silly, unsuspecting women.

Our lives had been extremely different the prior year, but both had been extremely difficult. I couldn't fully understand the complexity of what she was going through, and she couldn't fully understand the nuanced situation that had been my life. But none of that really mattered. In that moment, we simply listened to the other share. We asked about the loves in our lives, but we also made sure to give space to the question, "how are you doing?" It was in the space of that question that we were both able to put words to feelings and experiences we hadn't had a chance yet to identify. We gained a better understanding of ourselves because we spent time in community with one another.

When life is hard it is easy to justify sacrificing community for isolation. Sometimes, we even have good reasons to seek time alone: our exhaustion, our personality type, our depth of hurt, our need to process, or even our past history. But while healing happens in the quiet with our Creator, restoration happens within the community of His creation.

If we neglect to engage with others, we neglect a core aspect of our identity. Man was created in "our [the Trinity's] image" and was imprinted with an inherent essence of community in the process. I would even suggest that we cannot fully understand who we are without the context of community because it is such a core part of our design.

Unfortunately, our sinful nature likes to points out the flaws of community, as if it had no part in creating the fracture that made the sharp edges of relationships. It claims you need to protect yourself from the ragged points of conflict and throws around the lie that "people are annoying." So, we seek comfort in books, movies, podcasts, or anything else that helps us avoid other humans.

When we engage with others, we reflect the image of our Creator because He engaged with community. When we operate within our identity and purpose, we also find a sense of belonging. And the beautiful piece of this picture? Over time, as our sharp edges rub against the sharp edges of others within the safety of compassion, kindness, and humility, those edges become smooth.

rest in this truth:

How should I relate to those around me?
*With compassion because relationships
are ultimately a mirror by which we
understand our own design.*

day one: reflect

Reflect on the following question with
your Creator during your prayer time:

Do I seek community when life is hard?
Why or why not?

Jesus,_____

_____

_____

_____

_____

_____

_____

_____

_____

_____

_____

_____

_____

_____

_____ Amen.

day one: rest

List your concerns and requests below and
then turn them over to your Creator in
prayer, resting in His faithfulness.

Things on my mind today:

- _____
- _____
- _____
- _____
- _____

People on my mind today:

- _____
- _____
- _____
- _____
- _____

day two: reflect

*Reflect on the following question with
your Creator during your prayer time:*

What things do I choose over
engaging in relationships?

Jesus, _____

_____

_____

_____

_____

_____

_____

_____

_____

_____

_____

_____

_____

_____ Amen.

day two: rest

List your concerns and requests below and then turn them over to your Creator in prayer, resting in His faithfulness.

Things on my mind today:

- _____
- _____
- _____
- _____
- _____

People on my mind today:

- _____
- _____
- _____
- _____
- _____

day three: reflect

*Reflect on the following question with
your Creator during your prayer time:*

When was a time someone in my community offered
an insight that helped me understand
my identity or purpose?

Jesus, _____

_____

_____

_____

_____

_____

_____

_____

_____

_____

_____

_____

_____ Amen.

day three: rest

List your concerns and requests below and
then turn them over to your Creator in
prayer, resting in His faithfulness.

Things on my mind today:

- _____
- _____
- _____
- _____
- _____

People on my mind today:

- _____
- _____
- _____
- _____
- _____

day four: reflect

*Reflect on the following question with
your Creator during your prayer time:*

What hurts have I experienced from engaging in community
because it has been fractured by sin?

Jesus, _____

_____

_____

_____

_____

_____

_____

_____

_____

_____

_____

_____

_____

_____ Amen.

day four: rest

List your concerns and requests below and
then turn them over to your Creator in
prayer, resting in His faithfulness.

Things on my mind today:

- _____
- _____
- _____
- _____
- _____

People on my mind today:

- _____
- _____
- _____
- _____
- _____

day five: reflect

Have I forgiven past hurts from those within
my community? Why or why not?

Jesus, _____

_____

_____

_____

_____

_____

_____

_____

_____

_____

_____

_____

_____ Amen.

day five: rest

List your concerns and requests below and
then turn them over to your Creator in
prayer, resting in His faithfulness.

Things on my mind today:

- _____
- _____
- _____
- _____
- _____

People on my mind today:

- _____
- _____
- _____
- _____
- _____

day six: reflect

*Reflect on the following question with
your Creator during your prayer time:*

How can I be more intentional about inviting others into my life?

Jesus, _____

_____

_____

_____

_____

_____

_____

_____

_____

_____

_____

_____

_____

_____ Amen.

day six: rest

List your concerns and requests below and then turn them over to your Creator in prayer, resting in His faithfulness.

Things on my mind today:

- _____
- _____
- _____
- _____
- _____

People on my mind today:

- _____
- _____
- _____
- _____
- _____

sermon notes

speaker:

passage:

main points:

resources mentioned:

to further explore:

reflect: weekly lookback

Use this space to reflect on this past week
during your Sabbath reflection time.

what I embraced:

how God embraced me:

what I hope for next week:

reflect: dig deeper

This list of questions will be the same from week to week. Choose at least 3 questions that jump out to you (you can always do more!). Don't avoid the questions that seem harder to answer; sitting with your Creator with the hard questions is part of the practice of reflection.

who am I?

What did I spend my time doing this week?

What do I want to do more of?

What do I want to do less of?

What is something new I want to try this coming week?

What energized me this week?

What surprised me about myself this week?

who does God say I am?

What did God remind me about myself this week?

What rang true for me this week about who God says I am?

What did I have a hard time believing about my relationship with God this week?

What label did I give myself this week?

What God-given label do I want to speak over myself this week?

how should I live?

Where did I fall short this week?

Where has God been renewing and restoring in my life?

When did I use my God-given talents or giftings this week?

What do I want to converse with God about regarding my future?

What am I hesitant to discuss with God about my future? Why?

What step of obedience do I need to take this week?

how should I relate to those around me?

Who impacted me this week?

Who did I feel the most myself around this week?

Who do I want to be intentional in spending time with this coming week?

Who do I need to release?

How did I support my community this week?

How did my community support me this week?

reflect: dig deeper

Pick three questions from the list to the left to
guide you in further reflecting on certain aspects
of your identity, purpose, and belonging this week.

reflect: dig deeper

This space is for you to write down any
additional reflections you may
have from the week.

day seven: rest in His provision

As we close out this week of rest & reflection, note below where your Creator answered prayer and give thanks for His enduring love, forgiveness, and faithful provision.

Answered prayers:

- _____

- _____

- _____

Jesus, I thank you this week for:

- _____

- _____

- _____

a sabbath prayer

Jesus, thank you for the gift of Sabbath and the opportunity it gives to connect with you and with others. As this week draws to a close, open our eyes to those you've placed in our lives to walk alongside us in both our challenges and our dreams. May we acknowledge and receive their support. Please open our hearts to welcome those who need a friend. Open our ears to hear the hurts and needs of others so that we can help in whatever way we are able. And open our lips to speak truth, encouragement, and hope to those around us. Amen.

week 9

who am I?

> But now, O Lord, you are our Father; we are the clay, and you are our potter; we are all the work of your hand. Isaiah 64:8 (ESV)

You both end and begin in that pivotal moment of confession of faith. You end your ties with sin's damaging ramifications and begin living under the work of Christ on the cross. But, it's important to note that who you are at your core is the same prior to the moment you confessed Jesus as Lord as it is in the moments and years afterward.

I personally love to watch shows that follow the process of restoration, whether it's a piece of furniture or an entire house, I'm captivated from start to finish. First of all, I'm always impressed by the eye of the designer who sees the piece for its inherent value and the unique purpose it can serve. The amount of loving care they then pour into stripping away old paint, sanding down rough surfaces, oiling old hinges, replacing missing wood, etc. is mind-blowing to this girl with poor fine-motor skills. Then, they add on beautiful stain or paint and new finishings and the piece is not only restored to its original design, it has been been given a whole new glory.

If you haven't figured out where I'm going with this, let me spell it out: You are like an old furniture piece. You were intentionally designed and intentionally purposed, but living in a sinful, fractured world adds wear-and-tear and a layer of dust and grime. Christ's death on the cross was only the first step of the process; He paid the price with His death (that's what we call justification) and brought you home to begin the restorative process (that's what we call sanctification).

Justification is our salvation.
Sanctification is our restoration.

Justification is a state of being.
Sanctification is a state of doing.

Justification is stillness.
Sanctification is movement.

Justification required His wounds.
Sanctification requires our brokenness.

Justification is becoming right with God.
Sanctification is becoming more like God.

Justification is bestowed.
Sanctification is practiced.

Your design and purpose doesn't change throughout the process. The one who bought you with His life intimately knows your design and is actively working to restore you to the beautiful craftsmanship of His hands. If anyone should restore a piece, it should be the one who created it in the first place. You can trust Him with the process.

But, it is a process. And the refining can be hard. Know that as the layers of dust and grime are removed and your life begins to look more like your Creator's original design, which is to say one that looks more Christ-like, you will find a beautiful soul-renewing as it realigns with its identity and purpose.

rest in this truth:

Who am I?
I am a redeemed image of my Creator
in the process of being restored.

day one: reflect

Does it give me comfort to know my Creator is also
the one who is overseeing my restoration?
Why or why not?

Jesus, _____

_____

_____

_____

_____

_____

_____

_____

_____

_____

_____

_____ Amen.

day one: rest

List your concerns and requests below and
then turn them over to your Creator in
prayer, resting in His faithfulness.

Things on my mind today:

- _____
- _____
- _____
- _____
- _____

People on my mind today:

- _____
- _____
- _____
- _____
- _____

day two: reflect

*Reflect on the following question with
your Creator during your prayer time:*

Where in my life have I seen God working on me?

Jesus, _____

_____

_____

_____

_____

_____

_____

_____

_____

_____

_____

_____

_____

_____ Amen.

day two: rest

List your concerns and requests below and then turn them over to your Creator in prayer, resting in His faithfulness.

Things on my mind today:

- _____
- _____
- _____
- _____
- _____

People on my mind today:

- _____
- _____
- _____
- _____
- _____

day three: reflect

*Reflect on the following question with
your Creator during your prayer time:*

Where do I need to be more attentive to God's
restorative work in my life now?

Jesus, _____

_____

_____

_____

_____

_____

_____

_____

_____

_____

_____

_____

_____

_____ Amen.

day three: rest

List your concerns and requests below and
then turn them over to your Creator in
prayer, resting in His faithfulness.

Things on my mind today:

- _____
- _____
- _____
- _____
- _____

People on my mind today:

- _____
- _____
- _____
- _____
- _____

day four: reflect

*Reflect on the following question with
your Creator during your prayer time:*

What do I still need to understand about the difference
between justification and sanctification?

Jesus, _____

_____

_____

_____

_____

_____

_____

_____

_____

_____

_____

_____

_____ Amen.

day four: rest

List your concerns and requests below and
then turn them over to your Creator in
prayer, resting in His faithfulness.

Things on my mind today:

- _____
- _____
- _____
- _____
- _____

People on my mind today:

- _____
- _____
- _____
- _____
- _____

day five: reflect

*Reflect on the following question with
your Creator during your prayer time:*

Which spiritual discipline can I intentionally practice next week to foster growth (sanctification) in my life?

Jesus, _____

_____

_____

_____

_____

_____

_____

_____

_____

_____

_____

_____

_____ Amen.

day five: rest

List your concerns and requests below and then turn them over to your Creator in prayer, resting in His faithfulness.

Things on my mind today:

- _____
- _____
- _____
- _____
- _____

People on my mind today:

- _____
- _____
- _____
- _____
- _____

day six: reflect

*Reflect on the following question with
your Creator during your prayer time:*

What does it mean for me that I am living a life
that is in the process of being restored
instead of already perfected?

Jesus, _____

_____

_____

_____

_____

_____

_____

_____

_____

_____

_____

_____

_____ Amen.

day six: rest

List your concerns and requests below and
then turn them over to your Creator in
prayer, resting in His faithfulness.

Things on my mind today:

- _____
- _____
- _____
- _____
- _____

People on my mind today:

- _____
- _____
- _____
- _____
- _____

sermon notes

speaker:

passage:

main points:

resources mentioned:

to further explore:

reflect: weekly lookback

Use this space to reflect on this past week
during your Sabbath reflection time.

what I embraced:

how God embraced me:

what I hope for next week:

reflect: dig deeper

This list of questions will be the same from week to week. Choose at least 3 questions that jump out to you (you can always do more!). Don't avoid the questions that seem harder to answer; sitting with your Creator with the hard questions is part of the practice of reflection.

who am I?

What did I spend my time doing this week?

What do I want to do more of?

What do I want to do less of?

What is something new I want to try this coming week?

What energized me this week?

What surprised me about myself this week?

who does God say I am?

What did God remind me about myself this week?

What rang true for me this week about who God says I am?

What did I have a hard time believing about my relationship with God this week?

What label did I give myself this week?

What God-given label do I want to speak over myself this week?

how should I live?

Where did I fall short this week?

Where has God been renewing and restoring in my life?

When did I use my God-given talents or giftings this week?

What do I want to converse with God about regarding my future?

What am I hesitant to discuss with God about my future? Why?

What step of obedience do I need to take this week?

how should I relate to those around me?

Who impacted me this week?

Who did I feel the most myself around this week?

Who do I want to be intentional in spending time with this coming week?

Who do I need to release?

How did I support my community this week?

How did my community support me this week?

reflect: dig deeper

Pick three questions from the list to the left to
guide you in further reflecting on certain aspects
of your identity, purpose, and belonging this week.

reflect: dig deeper

*This space is for you to write down any
additional reflections you may
have from the week.*

_____

_____

_____

_____

_____

_____

_____

_____

_____

_____

_____

_____

_____

_____

_____

_____

_____

day seven: rest in His provision

As we close out this week of rest & reflection, note below where
your Creator answered prayer and give thanks for His enduring
love, forgiveness, and faithful provision.

Answered prayers:

- _____
- _____
- _____

Jesus, I thank you this week for:

- _____
- _____
- _____

a sabbath prayer

Jesus, as we physically rest today, may we spiritually rest in the
knowledge that your death and resurrection both satisfied and
redeemed. We thank you for the ways you continue to provide for our
needs on a daily basis. Your faithfulness is steadfast. Your love,
enduring. Thank you for the ways you are redeeming and making
right the world and our relationships within it. We long for the day
when creation will be restored to its original design. Until then, we
rest in your goodness, mercy, and grace. Amen.

week 10

who does God say I am?

You did not choose me, but I chose you and appointed you that you should go and bear fruit and that your fruit should abide, so that whatever you ask the Father in my name, he may give it to you. John 15:16 (ESV)

My younger sister is of the generation that puts stickers on their water bottles. By slapping on some labels, they bring a little bit of uniqueness and personalization to an everyday item. Sometimes, I wonder if we slap labels onto our identity in the same way?

We seek to find ways to describe our desires and reaction to the world around us, not only so we can communicate that to others and be better known by them, but also so we can wrap our mind around why we do what we do. We are not unique in this, the Apostle Paul wrote about it in his letter to the Romans. We're in a perpetual tug-of-war between our unique design, our fractured and sinful nature, and our redeemed state. Our existence in and of itself is a complexity, but add on layers of hurt, frustrations, and fears, and we're left with this chart that has too many arrows and conditions for it to be clear. So, we take a test and add the label it offers us.

Now, don't get me wrong, I love a good personality test as much as the next person, but I do think there is a tendency to take the results of a test and accept it as the God-honest-truth, even though we haven't even consulted God. There are some very wise people who have been able to analyze and capture human behavior into a if-this-than-that formula, but they cannot begin to comprehend the full story of every single human being. The basis for their tests are trends; they can give you a general sense of what people typically do, but only God can truly give you the insight you crave.

The other day I decided to list the labels that God uses in the Bible to describe me. I came up with:

Redeemed	Pursued	Known	Appointed
Loved	Rescued	Secure	Saved
Purposed	Priceless	Valuable	Deeply Desired
Molded	Free	Restored	Not Forgotten

I knew there were more, so I googled it and added:

New	Chosen	Workmanship	Victorious
Ambassador	Washed Clean	Saint	Steward
Child of God	Appointed	Called	Set-apart
Friend	A Temple	Accepted	Made Alive

This list could keep going, but I'm going to stop there. If you are anything like me, you might be thinking "Those labels don't actually give me a framework with which to engage the world." Here's the thing though, personality tests give us words to describe what we're seeing, but the labels of the Bible give us words to describe what God sees.

If we are to fully embrace our unique design, it's imperative that we look at our lives from the perspective of our Creator. I may be an extrovert, but if I don't view myself as a redeemed extrovert who is an Ambassador, Witness, and Steward, I miss the rounded out corners of my personality within the context of my purpose. I miss my unique design.

Don't miss the wholeness in your identity—who you are, who God says you are, what is your purpose, and where you belong—simply because you slap on a label.

rest in this truth:

Who does God say I am?
I am a uniquely designed and redeemed individual who is known, loved, and purposed.

day one: reflect

*Reflect on the following question with
your Creator during your prayer time:*

What labels have I used to define myself in the past?

Jesus, _____

_____

_____

_____

_____

_____

_____

_____

_____

_____

_____

_____ Amen.

day one: rest

List your concerns and requests below and
then turn them over to your Creator in
prayer, resting in His faithfulness.

Things on my mind today:

- _____
- _____
- _____
- _____
- _____

People on my mind today:

- _____
- _____
- _____
- _____
- _____

day two: reflect

What labels have I adapted after taking a personality test?

Jesus, _____

_____

_____

_____

_____

_____

_____

_____

_____

_____

_____

_____

_____

_____ Amen.

day two: rest

List your concerns and requests below and
then turn them over to your Creator in
prayer, resting in His faithfulness.

Things on my mind today:

- _____
- _____
- _____
- _____
- _____

People on my mind today:

- _____
- _____
- _____
- _____
- _____

day three: reflect

*Reflect on the following question with
your Creator during your prayer time:*

What labels have others given me? Have I accepted
those labels or rejected them?

Jesus, _____

_____

_____

_____

_____

_____

_____

_____

_____

_____

_____

_____

_____

_____ Amen.

day three: rest

List your concerns and requests below and then turn them over to your Creator in prayer, resting in His faithfulness.

Things on my mind today:

- _____
- _____
- _____
- _____
- _____

People on my mind today:

- _____
- _____
- _____
- _____
- _____

day four: reflect

Reflect on the following question with
your Creator during your prayer time:

Is there an identity-related label that I cling
to tighter than the ones God assigns me?

Jesus, _____

_____

_____

_____

_____

_____

_____

_____

_____

_____

_____

_____

_____ Amen.

day four: rest

List your concerns and requests below and
then turn them over to your Creator in
prayer, resting in His faithfulness.

Things on my mind today:

- _____
- _____
- _____
- _____
- _____

People on my mind today:

- _____
- _____
- _____
- _____
- _____

day five: reflect

Which of the labels given by God in the Bible about me
do I want to explore more in depth?

Jesus, _____

_____

_____

_____

_____

_____

_____

_____

_____

_____

_____

_____

_____ Amen.

day five: rest

List your concerns and requests below and
then turn them over to your Creator in
prayer, resting in His faithfulness.

Things on my mind today:

- _____
- _____
- _____
- _____
- _____

People on my mind today:

- _____
- _____
- _____
- _____
- _____

day six: reflect

*Reflect on the following question with
your Creator during your prayer time:*

This week, where did I catch myself using a label
for myself that God wouldn't use for me?

Jesus, _____

_____

_____

_____

_____

_____

_____

_____

_____

_____

_____

_____

_____

_____ Amen.

day six: rest

List your concerns and requests below and
then turn them over to your Creator in
prayer, resting in His faithfulness.

Things on my mind today:

- _____
- _____
- _____
- _____
- _____

People on my mind today:

- _____
- _____
- _____
- _____
- _____

sermon notes

speaker:

passage:

main points:

resources mentioned:

to further explore:

reflect: weekly lookback

Use this space to reflect on this past week
during your Sabbath reflection time.

what I embraced:

how God embraced me:

what I hope for next week:

reflect: dig deeper

This list of questions will be the same from week to week. Choose at least 3 questions that jump out to you (you can always do more!). Don't avoid the questions that seem harder to answer; sitting with your Creator with the hard questions is part of the practice of reflection.

who am I?

What did I spend my time doing this week?

What do I want to do more of?

What do I want to do less of?

What is something new I want to try this coming week?

What energized me this week?

What surprised me about myself this week?

who does God say I am?

What did God remind me about myself this week?

What rang true for me this week about who God says I am?

What did I have a hard time believing about my relationship with God this week?

What label did I give myself this week?

What God-given label do I want to speak over myself this week?

how should I live?

Where did I fall short this week?

Where has God been renewing and restoring in my life?

When did I use my God-given talents or giftings this week?

What do I want to converse with God about regarding my future?

What am I hesitant to discuss with God about my future? Why?

What step of obedience do I need to take this week?

how should I relate to those around me?

Who impacted me this week?

Who did I feel the most myself around this week?

Who do I want to be intentional in spending time with this coming week?

Who do I need to release?

How did I support my community this week?

How did my community support me this week?

reflect: dig deeper

Pick three questions from the list to the left to
guide you in further reflecting on certain aspects
of your identity, purpose, and belonging this week.

reflect: dig deeper

This space is for you to write down any
additional reflections you may
have from the week.

day seven: rest in His provision

As we close out this week of rest & reflection, note below where your Creator answered prayer and give thanks for His enduring love, forgiveness, and faithful provision.

Answered prayers:

- _____
- _____
- _____

Jesus, I thank you this week for:

- _____
- _____
- _____

a sabbath prayer

Jesus, as this week comes to an end, may we remember that you came to overcome the darkness of sin through your death and resurrection. You are our Sabbath rest. Your death and resurrection bought us our freedom. May we rest in the provision of your sacrifice, reflect on your goodness and faithfulness, and rejoice as children of God! Amen.

week 11

how should I live?

For David, after he had served God's purpose in his own generation, fell asleep, and was buried among his fathers and underwent decay. Act 13:36 (NASB)

I lost the ability to dream for a bit.

A number of personal and ministry-related situations came knocking with their demands back-to-back and I moved into a place of survival. It seemed ridiculous to entertain the question of what did I want the next five years to look like when I wasn't sure what was going to happen in the next five days. This deviation from my usual optimistic, joyfully-planning approach to life crept in slowly and unassumingly. It took up residence before I even realized I had invited it as a guest.

I was trusting God with my day-by-day, but I couldn't seem to trust Him with my day-dreaming. What changed? Wise voices from friends, family, and mentors reminding me of God's true heart. He isn't just in the job of supplying all our needs, He is the one who delights in us. The one who gives us good gifts. The one who created us with a set of skills and entrusted us with certain giftings. He is both purpose-giver and purpose-champion. He wants to see you succeed in living out your unique design and unique purpose, not only for His glory, but for your good.

Dreams can feel selfish or silly. But, I truly believe that our dreams, when explored in the sacred space of prayer and fasting, are insights into the identity, purpose, and belonging God uniquely designed for us.

Does that mean He makes all our dreams come true? Of course not. We are looking at our dreams through a fractured lens, remember? Which means, sometimes we don't fully understand the dream we wish for or the nuances that will accompany it. But, God knows.

I once asked Jesus to wait to return until I had experienced all that adulting had to offer. My teenage heart wanted to be married, be a mom, own a home, and publish a book. Those were my dreams. On this side of 18, I realize I didn't fully understand the depth of experience those dreams would usher into my life, but they were there and God, in His wisdom and purpose, had those for me to walk in. Nor did I understand all the good and extraordinary moments in my life that God lined up for me that my little mind could have never dreamed up. And, even more important, were the unrealized dreams that, with life-wisdom and God-revelation, I grew to understand would have been detrimental for me walk in. But, even the unrealized, not-so-great-for-me dreams taught me about my unique design, my sinful nature, and my redeemed state.

And what about those good dreams that haven't been granted yet or are taken away, as was the case when we miscarried last year? In those moments, we rest in the truth of God's faithful and good character, not in what He does or does not do.

May we stop praying "Lord, here is my dream, help me to accomplish it."

And instead pray: "Jesus, give me the wisdom to look at my dreams with your eyes, the courage to pursue the dreams that line up with your purposes, and the endurance to keep going when I'm tired. Let love permeate every step I take to fulfill any and all purposes you have for me in this generation. Don't cause my eyes to close in that final sleep until I have accomplished and been all that you designed me to do and be."

rest in this truth:

How should I live?
With an active embrace of my
God-aligned dreams.

day one: reflect

*Reflect on the following question with
your Creator during your prayer time:*

Have I talked to God about my dreams lately?
Why or why not?

Jesus, _____

_____

_____

_____

_____

_____

_____

_____

_____

_____

_____

_____

_____ Amen.

day one: rest

*List your concerns and requests below and
then turn them over to your Creator in
prayer, resting in His faithfulness.*

Things on my mind today:

- _____
- _____
- _____
- _____
- _____

People on my mind today:

- _____
- _____
- _____
- _____
- _____

day two: reflect

*Reflect on the following question with
your Creator during your prayer time:*

Am I willing to turn my dreams over to God and align
them with His purpose for my life? Why or why not?

Jesus, _____

_____

_____

_____

_____

_____

_____

_____

_____

_____

_____

_____

_____ Amen.

day two: rest

---

*List your concerns and requests below and
then turn them over to your Creator in
prayer, resting in His faithfulness.*

Things on my mind today:

- _____
- _____
- _____
- _____
- _____

People on my mind today:

- _____
- _____
- _____
- _____
- _____

day three: reflect

What is keeping me from pursuing my dreams?

Jesus, _____

_____

_____

_____

_____

_____

_____

_____

_____

_____

_____

_____

_____ Amen.

day three: rest

List your concerns and requests below and
then turn them over to your Creator in
prayer, resting in His faithfulness.

Things on my mind today:

- _____
- _____
- _____
- _____
- _____

People on my mind today:

- _____
- _____
- _____
- _____
- _____

day four: reflect

*Reflect on the following question with
your Creator during your prayer time:*

What is a dream that I need to set aside
time to fast and pray over?

Jesus, _____

_____

_____

_____

_____

_____

_____

_____

_____

_____

_____

_____

_____

_____ Amen.

day four: rest

List your concerns and requests below and then turn them over to your Creator in prayer, resting in His faithfulness.

Things on my mind today:

- _____
- _____
- _____
- _____
- _____

People on my mind today:

- _____
- _____
- _____
- _____
- _____

day five: reflect

*Reflect on the following question with
your Creator during your prayer time:*

What is a dream from my past that God
has reminded me of in recent months?

Jesus, _____

_____

_____

_____

_____

_____

_____

_____

_____

_____

_____

_____

_____

_____ Amen.

day five: rest

List your concerns and requests below and
then turn them over to your Creator in
prayer, resting in His faithfulness.

Things on my mind today:

- _____
- _____
- _____
- _____
- _____

People on my mind today:

- _____
- _____
- _____
- _____
- _____

day six: reflect

*Reflect on the following question with
your Creator during your prayer time:*

What one step of obedience do I need to do next to pursue my God-aligned dreams?

Jesus, _____

_____

_____

_____

_____

_____

_____

_____

_____

_____

_____

_____

_____

_____ Amen.

day six: rest

List your concerns and requests below and then turn them over to your Creator in prayer, resting in His faithfulness.

Things on my mind today:

- _____
- _____
- _____
- _____
- _____

People on my mind today:

- _____
- _____
- _____
- _____
- _____

sermon notes

speaker:

passage:

main points:

resources mentioned:

to further explore:

reflect: weekly lookback

Use this space to reflect on this past week
during your Sabbath reflection time.

what I embraced:

how God embraced me:

what I hope for next week:

reflect: dig deeper

This list of questions will be the same from week to week. Choose at least 3 questions that jump out to you (you can always do more!). Don't avoid the questions that seem harder to answer; sitting with your Creator with the hard questions is part of the practice of reflection.

who am I?

What did I spend my time doing this week?

What do I want to do more of?

What do I want to do less of?

What is something new I want to try this coming week?

What energized me this week?

What surprised me about myself this week?

who does God say I am?

What did God remind me about myself this week?

What rang true for me this week about who God says I am?

What did I have a hard time believing about my relationship with God this week?

What label did I give myself this week?

What God-given label do I want to speak over myself this week?

how should I live?

Where did I fall short this week?

Where has God been renewing and restoring in my life?

When did I use my God-given talents or giftings this week?

What do I want to converse with God about regarding my future?

What am I hesitant to discuss with God about my future? Why?

What step of obedience do I need to take this week?

how should I relate to those around me?

Who impacted me this week?

Who did I feel the most myself around this week?

Who do I want to be intentional in spending time with this coming week?

Who do I need to release?

How did I support my community this week?

How did my community support me this week?

reflect: dig deeper

Pick three questions from the list to the left to
guide you in further reflecting on certain aspects
of your identity, purpose, and belonging this week.

reflect: dig deeper

This space is for you to write down any
additional reflections you may
have from the week.

_____

_____

_____

_____

_____

_____

_____

_____

_____

_____

_____

_____

_____

_____

_____

_____

_____

day seven: rest in His provision

As we close out this week of rest & reflection, note below where your Creator answered prayer and give thanks for His enduring love, forgiveness, and faithful provision.

Answered prayers:

- _____
- _____
- _____

Jesus, I thank you this week for:

- _____
- _____
- _____

a sabbath prayer

Jesus, may we go into the new week remembering you are holy, good, and faithful. Through you, we have abundant life. Please provide for our needs this week and sustain us when challenges present themselves. Please bless us and draw us closer to you each and every day. Amen.

week 12

how should I relate to those around me?

> Let's not become discouraged in doing good, for in due time we will reap, if we do not become weary. So then, while we have opportunity, let's do good to all people, and especially to those who are of the household of the faith. Galatians 6:9-10 (NASB)

You are not meant to do this life alone. There is no crown at the pearly gates for the one who did the most on her own.

Just as Sabbath is a gift and guide for us, so is community.

I see you pulling back from my words and putting up your gate, placing you on one side and any (except for those select few you trust) and all other community on the other.

I hear you saying, "but, you don't know..."

And, "people are horrible."

And, "I don't belong."

Or, "I'm not wanted."

Let me rephrase: You cannot do this life alone. You were created with the imprint of community on your very soul.

Sin has not only hurt our people skills, our ability to love with compassion and understanding, our ability to support in good and helpful ways, and our ability to navigate conflict, it has altered a core aspect of our very essence. That's why it hurts so badly when you are both in Community and out of it. Sin has fractured our design.

It's time to reclaim it.

I could give you verse after verse about how community is necessary and good, but you already know that it is, even if you've been hurt by others in your life. You know, in your heart of hearts, that in order to fully live into this beautiful life God has for you, you need to surround yourself with people who are both cheering you on and whom you can cheer on.

People whom...

- you can be vulnerable with
- you can ask for prayer
- you can share your dreams with
- you can learn with
- you can play with
- you can worship alongside
- you can serve
- you can support

These are not necessarily all the same people! I only have a few key people in my life with whom I am vulnerable and share the different sides of my heart. These are people whom I know I can trust. Does this mean I am never hurt by them? No. It means I can trust that we will choose to look past hurt and disagreement and work towards reconciliation, no matter how hard it is.

Think about Jesus' time here on earth. What did His community look like? He had his inner circle (Peter, James, and John who witnessed the intimacy of the Mount of Transfiguration), His group of 12, others that traveled along with them, people he'd travel to visit (Mary, Martha, and Lazarus), and thousands and thousands that He worshiped alongside, served, and taught.

We are meant for community that looks like this. Real and robust. Layered and varied. A reflection of our Creator.

rest in this truth:

How should I relate to those around me?
Within the refining support of community.

day one: reflect

*Reflect on the following question with
your Creator during your prayer time:*

Who is in my inner circle? My cohort of 12?
My friendships and aquaintances?

Jesus, _____

_____

_____

_____

_____

_____

_____

_____

_____

_____

_____

_____

_____

_____ Amen.

day one: rest

List your concerns and requests below and
then turn them over to your Creator in
prayer, resting in His faithfulness.

Things on my mind today:

- _____
- _____
- _____
- _____
- _____

People on my mind today:

- _____
- _____
- _____
- _____
- _____

day two: reflect

Who in my life do I play with? Do I invest in that relationship?

Jesus, _____

_____

_____

_____

_____

_____

_____

_____

_____

_____

_____

_____

_____ Amen.

day two: rest

List your concerns and requests below and
then turn them over to your Creator in
prayer, resting in His faithfulness.

Things on my mind today:

- _____
- _____
- _____
- _____
- _____

People on my mind today:

- _____
- _____
- _____
- _____
- _____

day three: reflect

*Reflect on the following question with
your Creator during your prayer time:*

Who do I worship and pray alongside? Am I intentional
about requesting them to pray for me?

Jesus, _____

_____

_____

_____

_____

_____

_____

_____

_____

_____

_____

_____

_____ Amen.

day three: rest

List your concerns and requests below and then turn them over to your Creator in prayer, resting in His faithfulness.

Things on my mind today:

- _____
- _____
- _____
- _____
- _____

People on my mind today:

- _____
- _____
- _____
- _____
- _____

day four: reflect

Reflect on the following question with
your Creator during your prayer time:

Who can I trust with my dreams?
Have I shared with them lately?

Jesus, _____

_____

_____

_____

_____

_____

_____

_____

_____

_____

_____

_____

_____

_____ Amen.

day four: rest

*List your concerns and requests below and
then turn them over to your Creator in
prayer, resting in His faithfulness.*

Things on my mind today:

- _____
- _____
- _____
- _____
- _____

People on my mind today:

- _____
- _____
- _____
- _____
- _____

day five: reflect

*Reflect on the following question with
your Creator during your prayer time:*

Who in my life can I learn from? Am I being intentional
with that relationship? Why or why not?

Jesus, _____

_____

_____

_____

_____

_____

_____

_____

_____

_____

_____

_____

_____ Amen.

day five: rest

List your concerns and requests below and
then turn them over to your Creator in
prayer, resting in His faithfulness.

Things on my mind today:

- _____
- _____
- _____
- _____
- _____

People on my mind today:

- _____
- _____
- _____
- _____
- _____

day six: reflect

*Reflect on the following question with
your Creator during your prayer time:*

Who can I serve and support in my community?
Have I reached out to them lately?

Jesus, _____

_____

_____

_____

_____

_____

_____

_____

_____

_____

_____

_____

_____

_____ Amen.

day six: rest

List your concerns and requests below and then turn them over to your Creator in prayer, resting in His faithfulness.

Things on my mind today:

- _____
- _____
- _____
- _____
- _____

People on my mind today:

- _____
- _____
- _____
- _____
- _____

sermon notes

speaker:

passage:

main points:

resources mentioned:

to further explore:

reflect: weekly lookback

Use this space to reflect on this past week
during your Sabbath reflection time.

what I embraced:

how God embraced me:

what I hope for next week:

reflect: dig deeper

This list of questions will be the same from week to week. Choose at least 3 questions that jump out to you (you can always do more!). Don't avoid the questions that seem harder to answer; sitting with your Creator with the hard questions is part of the practice of reflection.

who am I?

What did I spend my time doing this week?

What do I want to do more of?

What do I want to do less of?

What is something new I want to try this coming week?

What energized me this week?

What surprised me about myself this week?

who does God say I am?

What did God remind me about myself this week?

What rang true for me this week about who God says I am?

What did I have a hard time believing about my relationship with God this week?

What label did I give myself this week?

What God-given label do I want to speak over myself this week?

how should I live?

Where did I fall short this week?

Where has God been renewing and restoring in my life?

When did I use my God-given talents or giftings this week?

What do I want to converse with God about regarding my future?

What am I hesitant to discuss with God about my future? Why?

What step of obedience do I need to take this week?

how should I relate to those around me?

Who impacted me this week?

Who did I feel the most myself around this week?

Who do I want to be intentional in spending time with this coming week?

Who do I need to release?

How did I support my community this week?

How did my community support me this week?

reflect: dig deeper

Pick three questions from the list to the left to
guide you in further reflecting on certain aspects
of your identity, purpose, and belonging this week.

reflect: dig deeper

*This space is for you to write down any
additional reflections you may
have from the week.*

_____

_____

_____

_____

_____

_____

_____

_____

_____

_____

_____

_____

_____

_____

_____

_____

_____

day seven: rest in His provision

As we close out this week of rest & reflection, note below where your Creator answered prayer and give thanks for His enduring love, forgiveness, and faithful provision.

Answered prayers:

- _____

- _____

- _____

Jesus, I thank you this week for:

- _____

- _____

- _____

a sabbath prayer

Jesus, thank you for the gift of Sabbath and the opportunity it gives to connect with you and with others. As this week draws to a close, open our eyes to those you've placed in our lives to walk alongside us in both our challenges and our dreams. May we acknowledge and receive their support. Please open our hearts to welcome those who need a friend. Open our ears to hear the hurts and needs of others so that we can help in whatever way we are able. And open our lips to speak truth, encouragement, and hope to those around us. Amen.

3-month look back

how do I embrace my unique design?

A plan in the heart of a person is like deep water,
but a person of understanding draws it out.
Proverbs 20:5 (ESV)

Many plans are in a person's heart, but the advice of
the Lord will stand. Proverbs 19:21 (ESV)

As our time together this quarter is drawing to a close, I want to take this week to ask the question: *How do I embrace my unique design?*

The answer is probably more simple than our "how-to" culture would like: You keep doing what you've been doing. Sit with your Creator and ask Him:

- Who am I and how has sin fractured my unique design?
- Who do you say I am?
- How should I live my life?
- How should I relate to those around me?

In your reflection time this week, you'll find questions to guide you in looking back over the last three months. It is good to pause and take account of what you've learned through the weekly practice of reflecting and conversing with your Creator.

I sincerely hope that this journal has given you the space to have those conversations, that it has helped you to understand yourself a bit better, given you a better understanding of how God sees you, and has deepened your relationship with Him. I hope you will continue this practice even after you turn the last page.

Remember, in humanity's story you are welcomed and your character is intentionally designed and uniquely purposed. You are not a mistake. You are not an anomaly. You were not just dropped into some storyline as an extra meant to take up space but make no real contribution.

Or worse yet, left on your own and forgotten. You are known by your Knower. His breath of life engaged your mind, your senses, your organs, and your very soul into existence.

Embrace your unique design.

rest in this truth:

How do I embrace my unique design?
One conversation with my Creator at a time.

day one: reflect

*Reflect on the following question with
your Creator during your prayer time:*

What have I learned these past 12 weeks about my
personality, talents, skills, and giftings?

Jesus,

Amen.

day one: rest

List your concerns and requests below and then turn them over to your Creator in prayer, resting in His faithfulness.

Things on my mind today:

- _____
- _____
- _____
- _____
- _____

People on my mind today:

- _____
- _____
- _____
- _____
- _____

day two: reflect

*Reflect on the following question with
your Creator during your prayer time:*

What have I learned in the past 12 weeks about the ways
in which my unique design been fractured by sin?

Jesus, _____

_____

_____

_____

_____

_____

_____

_____

_____

_____

_____

_____

_____

_____ Amen.

day two: rest

*List your concerns and requests below and
then turn them over to your Creator in
prayer, resting in His faithfulness.*

Things on my mind today:

- _____
- _____
- _____
- _____
- _____

People on my mind today:

- _____
- _____
- _____
- _____
- _____

day three: reflect

Reflect on the following question with
your Creator during your prayer time:

What lies about myself was I believing before I
started this time of rest and reflection?

Jesus, _____

_____

_____

_____

_____

_____

_____

_____

_____

_____

_____

_____

_____

_____ Amen.

day three: rest

List your concerns and requests below and
then turn them over to your Creator in
prayer, resting in His faithfulness.

Things on my mind today:

- _____
- _____
- _____
- _____
- _____

People on my mind today:

- _____
- _____
- _____
- _____
- _____

day four: reflect

*Reflect on the following question with
your Creator during your prayer time:*

What truths about my purpose did I learn in the past 12 weeks?

Jesus, _____

_____

_____

_____

_____

_____

_____

_____

_____

_____

_____

_____

_____ Amen.

day four: rest

List your concerns and requests below and
then turn them over to your Creator in
prayer, resting in His faithfulness.

Things on my mind today:

- _____
- _____
- _____
- _____
- _____

People on my mind today:

- _____
- _____
- _____
- _____
- _____

day five: reflect

Reflect on the following question with
your Creator during your prayer time:

Which dreams and goals became clearer in the past 12 weeks?

Jesus, _____

_____

_____

_____

_____

_____

_____

_____

_____

_____

_____

_____

_____

_____ Amen.

day five: rest

---

*List your concerns and requests below and
then turn them over to your Creator in
prayer, resting in His faithfulness.*

Things on my mind today:

- _____
- _____
- _____
- _____
- _____

People on my mind today:

- _____
- _____
- _____
- _____
- _____

day six: reflect

*Reflect on the following question with
your Creator during your prayer time:*

What did I learn over the past 12 weeks about my
relationships and my role in them?

Jesus, _____

_____

_____

_____

_____

_____

_____

_____

_____

_____

_____

_____

_____

_____

_____

_____ Amen.

day six: rest

List your concerns and requests below and
then turn them over to your Creator in
prayer, resting in His faithfulness.

Things on my mind today:

- _____
- _____
- _____
- _____
- _____

People on my mind today:

- _____
- _____
- _____
- _____
- _____

sermon notes

speaker:

passage:

main points:

resources mentioned:

to further explore:

reflect: 3-month lookback

Use this space to reflect on the past 12
weeks during your Sabbath reflection time.

what I embraced:

how God embraced me:

the next step of obedience I need to take:

reflect: dig deeper

As we continue to reflect over the past 12 weeks, choose at least 3 questions that jump out to you (you can always do more!).
You don't need perfect answers, just honest reflection.

who am I?

What did I spend my time doing?

What do I want to do more of?

What do I want to do less of?

What is something new I want to try in the future?

What energized me?

What surprised me about myself?

who does God say I am?

What did God teach me about myself these past 12 weeks?

What rang true these past 12 weeks about who God says I am?

What am I still having a hard time believing about my relationship with God ?

What labels do I need to still work to remove?

What God-given label do I want to speak over myself consistently?

how should I live?

How has God been renewing and restoring in my life these past 12 weeks?

When did I use my God-given talents or giftings?

What do I want to converse with God about regarding my future?

What am I hesitant to discuss with God about my future? Why?

how should I relate to those around me?

Who do I want to continue being intentional in spending time with in the future?

Who did I release? Who do I still need to release?

How did I support my community in the past 12 weeks?

How did my community support me in the past 12 weeks?

reflect: dig deeper

Pick three questions from the list to the left to
guide you in further reflecting on certain aspects
of your identity, purpose, and belonging this week.

reflect: dig deeper

This space is for you to write down any
additional reflections you may
have from the week.

day seven: rest in His provision

As we close out this 12-week rhythm of rest & reflection, note below where your Creator answered prayer and give thanks for His enduring love, forgiveness, and faithful provision.

Answered prayers:

- _____

- _____

- _____

Jesus, I thank you this week for:

- _____

- _____

- _____

a sabbath prayer

Jesus, as we physically rest today, may we spiritually rest in the knowledge that your death and resurrection both satisfied and redeemed. We thank you for the ways you continue to provide for our needs on a daily basis. Your faithfulness is steadfast. Your love, enduring. Thank you for the ways you are redeeming and making right the world and our relationships within it. We long for the day when creation will be restored to its original design. Until then, we rest in your goodness, mercy, and grace. Amen.

about the author

Rachel Fahrenbach is a storyteller learning to embrace her unique design. Through her writing, she invites you to see the gift of Sabbath as a guide for discovering your sense of identity, purpose, and belonging.

Rachel is no stranger to being different. She grew up outside of the normal-sized family unit (she is the oldest of 8 siblings), the typical school education (former homeschooler over here), the common secular outlook on life (God has had the final say in her life for a long time now), and the usual way of experiencing the world around her (the day she learned to use the word "creative" as a noun changed everything).

Learning to embrace her unique design has been a journey. Sometimes it has been easy (like when she majored in Creative Writing and Business Management) and other times it has been hard (she has wasted way too much time agonizing over what others think of her). But, through it all, her Creator has shown her His intentionality in her life.

And now, she helps others implement a weekly Sabbath practice that gives space to the questions "who am I" and "why am I here?" She thinks it's a pretty cool gig, but then again, that's how she's designed.

Rachel and her husband live in the Chicagoland area with their three kiddos.

Connect with Rachel:

rachelfahrenbach.com
instagram.com/rachelfahrenbach
rachel@rachelfahrenbach.com

acknowledgements

I debated if I should include an acknowledgments page in a guided journal. It's not quite a book, so it seemed perhaps a bit much, but this project is something more than just a few pages strung together with some words, and so it felt as if it warranted one.

What ultimately convinced me was the large number of people who in some way shaped this book for you, the reader. To not acknowledge the community that contributed to a journal that makes mention often of living out your purpose within community seemed like a swing and a miss.

So, here we go.

My Inner Circle

Steve - Thank you for always allowing me to dream out loud with you. The morning after I late-night brain dumped what would eventually become this journal, a rainbow wall of post-it notes greeted you. But you didn't even bat an eye. Instead, you asked me how you could help me reach my goals. We're a team, and I couldn't have done this without you.

Payton, Carter, and Trevor - Thank you so much for being patient with me as I finished this project. And thank you for being my biggest cheerleaders! "My journey starts and ends with you," and I love you very much!

Mom & Dad - Without the truths you taught me growing up (and even now in adulthood), I would not be able to share those truths with others through writing. Yours are the voices that always remind me of my true identity and the ears that listen to all my contemplations—even the crazy ones!

Erin, Erik, Taylor, Krissa, Ceilidh, Collin, Riley, Delaney, and Addison - You make conversations about identity, purpose, and belonging interesting and fun! My favorite place is sitting around the table with you.

Riley, Delaney, and Addison, you deserve an extra shoutout; honestly, without your willingness to watch my kids so I could write, this journal would never come to fruition. And Delaney, without you, my kitchen would have always been a pile of dirty dishes and my kids would never have any verses to say at Awana.

Jessica Binger Bejnar - You were the first one who pointed out to me that my creative-bent was a direct reflection of my Creator and I will forever be grateful for that. I know that you are always praying for me and only a phone call away.

My Cohort

My mastermind group, Jenn Uren, Jen Jao, and Michele Holmes - You ladies get me. Thank you for the countless number of Marco Polo messages throughout this journal's creation. From brainstorming content to proof-reading to cheering me across the finish line, and all the things in between, thank you.

My church small group, especially our fearless leaders Aaron and Wendy - For checking in with me and for praying as I worked towards deadlines, and for letting me process some of my theological thoughts out loud with you before writing them down.

My Hope*Writers peeps - Your encouragement, knowledge, and feedback have been invaluable. Thank you for showing up to support me as a writer week after week. A special thanks to Pamela Henkelman who told me to "teach us how you do your Sabbath reflections" (followed by quite a few exclamation points) and essentially set this journal into motion.

Friendships & Acquaintances

Kim Blain, Judith Barillas, Jolene Fellhauer, Hannah Hanson, Lodie Hards, Becca Meek, Tammie Phillips, Katherine Smith, Angela Trusty, and Kristina Wessels - Thank you, ladies, for being the first eyes on this journal's devotionals and offering your honest feedback. It made this journal better.

The Hope*Writers community - For your feedback on cover design and your knowledge of and training on all things publishing. A special thank you to Emily Allen, Jennifer Denney, and Sara Ward for answering my numerous questions and pointing me in the right direction.

My business and marketing coach, Brian Dixon - Your coaching helped me not only clarify my message but also get it out into the world. Thank you.

My Instagram followers who faithfully read the words I put out there - Thank you for your support, it means so much to me!

And in a category all His own, my Creator - Thank you for meeting me in the rest of Sabbath and teaching me what it means to be uniquely designed and uniquely purposed. It has been a gift and a guide and I am so grateful and humbled that you desire to dwell with me, your creation.

resources

You can find additional resources to help you implement a weekly Sabbath practice that gives space to discovering your identity, purpose, and belonging at:

rachelfahrenbach.com/journal-resources

Connect with Rachel:

rachelfahrenbach.com

instagram.com/rachelfahrenbach

rachel@rachelfahrenbach.com